HISTORIC SCOTLAND

THE REPAIR OF
HISTORIC BUILDINGS
IN SCOTLAND

Advice on principles and methods

1995

THE REPAIR OF HISTORIC BUILDINGS IN SCOTLAND
Advice on principles and methods

First published 1991 as The Repair of Historic Buildings:
Advice on principles and methods Christopher Brereton,
Copyright ©1991, 1995 English Heritage,
Fortress House, 23 Savile Row, London, W1X AB6

This edition: The Repair of Historic Buildings in Scotland:
Advice on principles and methods Ed. John Knight
Printed by HMSO on behalf of Historic Scotland
HISTORIC SCOTLAND.
Longmore House
Salisbury Place
Edinburgh EH9 1SH
Copyright ©1995 Historic Scotland. Joint copyright with English Heritage
A CIP record for this book is available from the British Library

ISBN 0 9517989 2 9

PREFACE

Historic Scotland can trace its descent from the Office of the King's Works, through various successors to its present status as the executive agency of the Scottish Office responsible for the protection and presentation of Scotland's built heritage. On behalf of the Secretary of State, it administers legislation pertaining to some 6,000 Scheduled Ancient Monuments and 40,000 Listed Buildings, including providing grant aid for repairs to owners and caring for some 330 monuments in State guardianship. As part of this, it maintains a register of conservators, has its own specialised experts and produces educational publications about the built heritage and technical aspects of conservation.

These advice notes are closely based on the English Heritage publication "The Repair of Historic Buildings" by Christopher Brereton and follow it verbatim where Scottish and English restoration and repair methods are to all intents and purposes the same. Scottish building terminology has however been substituted where appropriate, and the sections on thatching, harling, the repair of earth walls, and the repair of glass have been re-written. Other sections have been updated to take advantage of current information and improved knowledge, but changes where they occur generally reflect the nuances of conservation practice in Scotland and limit the advice to the Scottish situation. A new section on Energy Conservation and Disaster Planning has been added. The illustrations show local examples, and the Scottish version has been edited by John Knight, with contributions from Pat Gibbons, Robin Kent and Bruce Walker.

Designed to complement Historic Scotland's Memorandum of Guidance on Listed Buildings and Conservation Areas, with a greatly increased technical content, it has been produced by the Technical Conservation, Research and Education Division of Historic Scotland. It will be of value to designers, owners, authorities and craftsmen, in fact, to all concerned with the authentic repair of historic buildings in Scotland. It will also provide a resource for educational providers in the field of practical conservation. While its production started out as a joint venture between the two organisations, Historic Scotland acknowledges that English Heritage has kindly allowed it to adopt and use the bulk of Christopher Brereton's text, and so directly benefit from the effort and considerable expertise that he put into writing the book before his untimely death in 1992.

INGVAL MAXWELL
Director
Technical Conservation, Research and Education Division
Historic Scotland

Edinburgh, August, 1995

CONTENTS

1

INTRODUCTION

The purpose of this volume is to provide guidance to building owners and their professional advisers on the principles which should be applied in the repair of historic buildings and monuments, and on the methods which are appropriate to the observance of those principles.

The book (and its English Heritage predecessors) has been prepared in order to satisfy a long-standing demand for such guidance - both from English Heritage and Historic Scotland (HS) - and with the aim of achieving a consistency of approach in historic building repairs.

The basic principles and objectives which are relevant to an individual case should be established at the outset, and should then be applied to generate the solution to the particular problem and method of repair.

It is essential to identify causes before specifying remedies and in pursuit of this there is a need for a careful and accurate diagnosis including, where appropriate, monitoring of the structure.

The recommendations on methods of repair are intended for guidance only and should be considered in the context of a careful analysis of the needs of a particular building. There can be no standard specification for the repair of historic buildings and monuments.

It is important to continue to look at a building as work proceeds, in case the nature of some of the repairs is found to change, with the result that methods may need to be revised.

Perhaps most important of all are the attitudes and degree of sensitivity of building owners, their professional advisers and those working on site.

Chatelherault, near Hamilton: a major Scottish repair and restoration project completed in 1987, that employed almost all the techniques described in this book.

2

PRINCIPLES OF REPAIR

Chatelherault: careful retention of sound original fabric and accurate reinstatement of lost features in accordance with documentary evidence.

2.1 THE PURPOSE OF REPAIR

The primary purpose of repair is to restrain the process of decay without damaging the character of buildings or monuments, altering the features which give them their historic or architectural importance, or unnecessarily disturbing or destroying historic fabric.

2.2 THE NEED FOR REPAIR

Works of repair should be kept to the minimum required to stabilise and conserve buildings and monuments, with the aim of achieving a sufficiently sound structural condition to ensure their long-term survival.

2.3 AVOIDING UNNECESSARY DAMAGE

The authenticity of an historic building depends most crucially on the integrity of its fabric and on its design, which may be original or may incorporate different periods of addition and alteration. The unnecessary replacement of historic fabric, no matter how carefully the work is carried out, will have an adverse effect on the appearance of a building or monument, will seriously diminish its authenticity, and will significantly reduce its value as a source of historical information. Inevitably, elements of the fabric will decay or become defective in other ways, but the rate and extent to which this occurs will vary. For example, certain types of roof covering and protective wall covering will require periodic complete or major replacement. Other elements, in particular masonry and the framing of timber roofs, are more likely to decay slowly and in parts, rather than comprehensively, and will require a more selective approach.

2.4 ANALYSING HISTORIC DEVELOPMENT

A thorough understanding of the historical development of a building or monument is a necessary preliminary to its repair. This may involve specialised archeological and architectural investigations, documentary research, recording and interpretation of the particular structure, and its assessment in a wider historic context. Such processes may, when appropriate, need to continue during the course of repairs. Satisfactory arrangements should be made for the subsequent preservation of all records, including quotations and invoices etc., and any professional reports. (See 3 Maintenance and minor repairs).

2.5 ANALYSING THE CAUSES OF DEFECTS

In addition to an analysis of the historic development of the building or monument, the detailed design of repairs should also be preceded by a survey including long term observation of any structural defects, an investigation of the nature and condition of its materials and of the causes, processes, and rates of decay. To repair or replace decayed fabric without first carrying out such investigations could be to invite the repetition of problems.

2.6 ADOPTING PROVEN TECHNIQUES

Repair techniques should be matched to or be compatible with existing materials and methods of construction, in order to preserve the appearance and historic integrity of the building or monument, and to ensure that the work has an appropriate life. Exceptions should only be considered where the existing fabric has failed because of inherent defects of design or incorrect specification of materials, rather than from neglect of maintenance or because it has completed its expected life. New methods and techniques should only be used where they have proved themselves over a sufficient period, where traditional alternatives cannot be identified, or where the use of modern methods enables important features to be retained. In deciding whether to adopt new methods and techniques it will be necessary to balance the degree of benefit to the building or monument in the future against any damage which may be caused to its appearance or historic integrity.

Cement mortar patching of decayed carved stone, which has led to further erosion.

2.7 TRUTH TO MATERIALS

Repairs should be executed honestly, respecting the character of the historic fabric, usually with no attempt at disguise or artificial ageing. They should not be unnecessarily obtrusive or unsympathetic in appearance. When the replacement of historic fabric is unavoidably extensive, or significant in other ways, the work should be discreetly dated for future reference.

2.8 REMOVAL OF LATER ALTERATIONS

Additions or alterations, including earlier repair, are of importance for the part they play in the cumulative history of a building or monument. There should always be a strong presumption in favour of their retention. Whilst a programme of repairs may offer the opportunity for removing features which

Botching of decayed ashlar stonework with cement mortar.

3

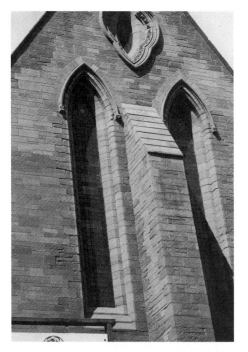

Chatelherault: the replacement, as part of a comprehensive programme of repair, of missing urns and ball finials which were an important part of the original design of this eye catching building.

Wholesale replacement rather than random repair has resulted in loss of historic integrity, despite accurate copying of details

are of no intrinsic value in themselves, and which seriously disrupt the architectural design and aesthetic value of a building or monument, the full implications of doing so must be carefully considered in advance, and potential architectural and aesthetic gains need to be balanced against any likely loss of historic integrity. Work of this kind should be carefully measured and recorded and the necessary statutory consents must be obtained in advance.

2.9   RESTORATION OF LOST FEATURES

Some elements of a building or monument which are important to its design, for example balustrades, pinnacles, cornices, hoodmoulds, window tracery, and members of a timber frame or roof truss, may have been lost in the past. Where these are of structural significance, they should be put back in the course of repair; but a programme of repair may also offer the opportunity for the reinstatement of missing non-structural elements, provided that sufficient evidence exists for accurate replacement, no loss of historic fabric occurs, and the necessary statutory consents are obtained in advance. Conjectural reconstruction or restoration is seldom justifiable.

2.10   SAFEGUARDING THE FUTURE

An historic building or monument should be regularly monitored and maintained, and wherever possible provided with an appropriate and sympathetic use. This is the best way of securing its future, and of keeping further repair requirements to a minimum.

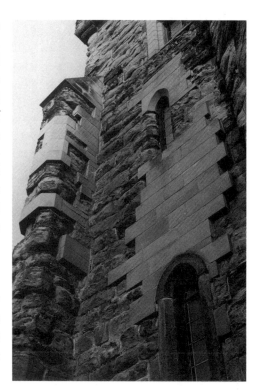

Heavily eroded masonry requires a sensitive approach to ensure repairs are not obtrusive.

3

MAINTENANCE AND MINOR REPAIRS

The best means of ensuring the continued preservation of a building is to carry out regular maintenance. Such work is part of the day-to-day responsibility of all owners and occupiers.

Maintenance most crucially concerns those elements which protect a building from water and damp penetration, in particular roof coverings, rhones, gutters, rhonepipes, gullies and perimeter drains, and also open joints in masonry, cracked render etc.

The best way of monitoring the need for and effectiveness of maintenance, and also of assessing when major repairs are required, is to institute a system of periodic detailed inspection of the building by a suitably qualified professional who will prepare a report with recommendations. Such an inspection should be carried out at least every 5 years. The preparation and regular updating of a maintenance and repair diary, supplemented with key drawings, photographs, etc., will be a valuable source of reference for all those responsible for a building now and in the future.

Maintenance may be divided into 2 main categories: first, that which depends on the day-to-day vigilance of the building owner and can usually be dealt with without the need to employ outside labour; and second, that which is in the nature of minor repair and is best carried out on an annual basis by a builder who has knowledge of and sympathy towards historic building construction. It should be noted, however, that even such relatively minor works will benefit from being overseen by a qualified professional. Expenditure on fees is usually offset by improved cost control and a higher standard of work, with longer-lasting effects.

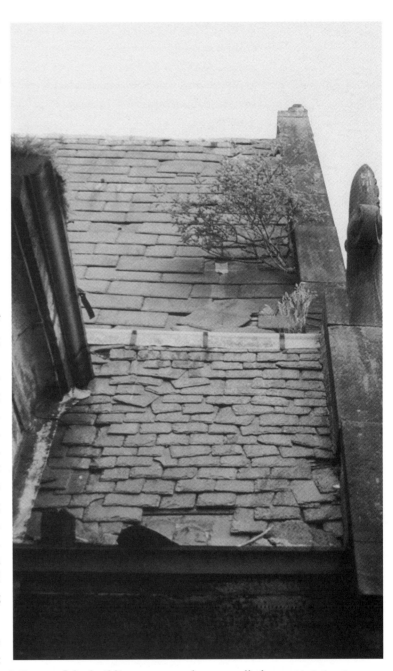

Blocked and overgrown gutters, cracked fillets, slipped slates and vegetation are signs of persisitently neglected maintenance. (photo: I. Maxwell)

3.1   DAY-TO-DAY MAINTENANCE

3.1.1   CLEARING LEAVES

Clear leaves, accumulated silt etc., from gutters (including parapet and valley gutters), flat roofs, rhonepipes, gullies, perimeter drainage channels etc. This should be done about every 3 months and particularly during and after the autumn fall of leaves. This is probably the single most important operation and if neglected, will soon be the cause of major defects. Faults in rainwater goods, etc. are most readily identified during heavy rain. Where access is difficult, fixed ladders, hatches, etc. should be installed in convenient but unobtrusive positions.

3.1.2   CLEARING SNOW

Clear snow from valley and parapet gutters, flat roofs etc., to prevent it from building up above the level of sheet laps and flashings, and to prevent water which is flowing below thawing snow from refreezing and blocking outlets. Wooden or plastic shovels should be used, since great care is needed to avoid damaging leadwork, slating etc. Duckboards should be provided for access and will facilitate the flow of meltwater in valley and parapet gutters. Electric heating tapes with temperature and moisture sensors can be effective at keeping concealed valleys clear.

3.1.3   CONTROLLING PLANT GROWTH

Destruction of a coursed rubble wall by ivy.

Control plant growth on masonry and around the perimeter of the building, and remove it where it is causing damage. This should be done at an early stage before roots get a hold and penetrate deeply into a wall. If ivy has been allowed to grow, it should be killed by cutting through the stem near the ground and applying a poisonous paste. The upper part should be left to die before it is carefully detached from the wall. Alternatively, poisoning the ivy through its root system may more effectively ensure that the root is killed.

When plant growth is removed from the ground around the perimeter of a building, it is important to ensure that the ground level is maintained so as not to allow either the progressive exposure of the wall base and foundations, or the build-up of ground levels.

3.1.4   REMOVING BIRD DROPPINGS

Remove accumulations of bird droppings. Internally, in church towers, attics etc., droppings can contribute to timber decay. Loose bird guards should be refixed to prevent access. Any defective steel mesh guards should be replaced in non-ferrous material. A proprietary system employing stainless steel 'piano' wire secured by non-ferrous pins set into joints can prove an effective deterrent to birds. Externally, on masonry, droppings can produce damaging salts and promote disfiguring biological growths. Care should be taken to observe the necessary health and safety precautions when removing bird droppings.

3.1.5 LOOKING FOR INSECT AND FUNGAL ATTACK

Check for signs of active insect or fungal attack in timbers and, if this is suspected, inform your architect or an independent consultant; a specialist firm, which has a vested interest in carrying out treatment, may recommend more extensive treatment than is strictly necessary. (See 4.6 Repair of structural timbers).

3.2 MINOR REPAIRS AND MAINTENANCE INVOLVING BUILDERS WORKS

3.2.1 MINOR WORKS TO SLATE AND TILE ROOFS

Patch repairs should be carried out by refixing loose and slipped slates and tiles and replacing broken ones with matching material, ensuring the substrate is suitably sound for slating nails.

Excess moss should be carefully removed as this can harbour damp, causing slates and tiles to delaminate. (See also 3.2.2).

Bitumen-coated fabric applied over roofs or spray-on coating systems on the underside of roofs where sarking does not occur should not be used. They prevent sound slates or tiles from being salvaged for reuse when comprehensive roof repairs are eventually undertaken. Also, when subsequent defects occur, they are difficult to locate and make good. Such treatments may also have the effect of sealing roof voids and preventing ventilation, with the consequent risk of fungal attack and rot of roof timbers.

3.2.2 REPAIR OF EXISTING LEADWORK AND OTHER METAL COVERINGS

Individual worn-out sheets should be replaced, and splits in rhones and gutters which have some years of life remaining should be repaired before complete stripping and removal become necessary. Holes and splits should be properly repaired with lead-welded patches, not by the use of solder. This should be carried out by a qualified plumber and with stringent fire precautions (See 5.2 Fire Prevention). Bitumen-coated fabrics, other bituminised treatments or tapes should never be used. They conceal later developing faults in the lead and inhibit the carrying out of permanent repairs. Their effective life is short, as exposure to ultra-violet radiation results in degradation.

Rain falling on moss or lichen-covered slate or tile roofs can discharge as an acidic run-off, causing holes or channels in metal roof coverings below. Sacrificial flashings may be provided where the run-off occurs, or, as an additional precaution, copper wire may be fixed across the roof slope in order to create a copper salt wash during rainfall which will inhibit the growth of moss or lichen.

Zinc, copper, stainless steel, or aluminium roofs are, because of their lighter weight, more prone to damage by wind-lift. Should this occur, it should be dealt with immediately by refixing at seams or ridges, otherwise cracking and general failure caused by "working" in the wind may necessitate complete replacement. Other minor

defects may be temporarily dealt with by fixing patches of matching metal secured by a waterproof adhesive.

3.2.3 REFIXING SLIPPED LEAD OR OTHER METAL FLASHINGS

This will be necessary at gable and chimney abutments, parapets, etc., as will be the replacement of short lengths of flashing in matching material where they are split or holed. Vertical splits may be covered with matching material and wedged and pointed above the original flashing. (See 4.2.2).

3.2.4 MAINTENANCE OF THATCH

Thatch in Scotland may be of a wide range of traditional materials. Roofs should be regularly inspected and local repairs carried out in a matching material by an experienced thatcher. (See Thatch 4.2.3).

3.2.5 MAINTENANCE OF GUTTERS, RHONES AND RHONEPIPES

Maintenance includes the de-rusting and painting of cast-iron rainwater goods and replacement of short, broken, and split lengths in matching material, not in pvc. Rectangular cast-iron rhonepipes should be particularly carefully maintained as they are liable to rust unseen at the back. Rhonepipes should be repainted and refixed on spacers sufficiently clear of the wall to allow for a free flow of air and also for inspection and painting.

Where rhonepipes are connected directly into drains (ie. without gullies) they are liable to become blocked, allowing the pipes to fill with water and freeze, causing cracking. Gullies should therefore be provided (not back-inlet) in order to allow for the rodding of rainwater pipes and drains, and inspection covers/hand-holes provided as necessary.

Cast-iron rhones which sit on stone corbelled eaves courses are particularly vulnerable to rusting on their undersides and backs, and it may be wise to wedge them up clear of the stone to allow evaporation of moisture below. Where joints have failed, the gutter should be dismantled to remake them and before reinstating, a flashing may be laid under the gutter as an additional precaution.

Lead downpipes, hopper heads, and sometimes cast-iron hopper heads can be of historic interest or important features of a building and if damaged, should be carefully overhauled rather than replaced. (See 4.3 Renewal of rainwater goods).

Faults in rainwater goods will soon lead to saturation of adjacent areas of wall. Overflows are useful for directing spillage away from the building and indicating where there are blocked heads and pipes. If maintenance is neglected mortar will be washed out of joints in masonry, plant growth will develop, and serious structural

Unless this rusting and leaking cast-iron rhone pipe, supporting extensive vegetation, is dealt with, the adjacent stone work will be seriously damaged by water saturation and will put at risk any timbers built into the structure.

problems may arise. Moisture transference to the interior can cause significant damage and is usually the cause of dry or wet rot originating in associated timber.

3.2.6 MAINTENANCE OF PERIMETER DRAINAGE CHANNELS, FRENCH DRAINS, OR GROUND GUTTERS

These are most commonly found around churches and are often a source of trouble, since cracks or open joints will allow considerable amounts of water to seep into the foundations (affecting their stability in due course), and will also cause rising damp in walls (affecting internal finishes and fittings). Cracks should therefore be pointed wherever they occur, but it is preferable to remove channels and replace them with a system of gullies below the downpipes, connected to drains, taking care to route between graves etc. French drains should be regularly checked to ensure they are functioning, as they may require clearing and re-laying.

3.2.7 RODDING AND SUBSEQUENT INSPECTION OF UNDERGROUND STORM WATER DRAINS

Any necessary minor repairs should be made to short lengths of drain.

3.2.8 MINOR AREAS OF REPOINTING OF STONEWORK AND BRICKWORK

Much harder, cementious, pointing has contributed to the extensive decay of the brickwork.
(photo: I. Maxwell)

Small, isolated areas of repointing should be dealt with regularly as items of maintenance, but only where joints are open or mortar is loose; sound old pointing should always be left undisturbed. It is important that repointing is done correctly using a lime/sand mortar, not a cement/sand mortar, to avoid damage to the appearance and character, as well as the structure of a building. Inappropriate mortar mixes and finishes

of joints in pointing can cause significant damage by being too strong for the masonry and can cause disfigurement to the appearance of a building. (See 4.9 Repointing of stonework and brickwork for advice on repointing).

3.2.9 MAINTENANCE OF EXTERNAL RENDER AND HARLING

Old lime renders and harling, sometimes self-finished in the case of the former, and sometimes limewashed in the case of the latter, have an attractive character and may be of historical interest. Their life should be prolonged for as long as possible by correct maintenance, with patch repairs in a carefully matched mix at cracked or loose areas, and when appropriate by regular re-limewashing.

Harder renders used in the nineteenth and twentieth centuries also need regular maintenance if they are not to fail rapidly due to water penetration through cracks. They are often painted, but where self-finished a successful match of colour and texture may be difficult, and is best achieved by the correct choice of sand. The addition of pigment is always inadvisable as these tend to fade and weather differently in time. (See 4.12 Repair of external render and harling for advice on repair of renders).

3.2.10 PREVENTATIVE TREATMENT OF TIMBER AGAINST INSECT AND FUNGAL ATTACK

Prevention is best achieved by ensuring that the timber is kept dry and well ventilated. When insect attack occurs, it can be kept at bay by the periodic use of insecticides at the time of emergence of the insect in the spring, but also by the avoidance of warm, poorly ventilated spaces which can encourage breeding. If preservative fluids are used they should be colourless, and care taken to avoid damage to historic surfaces and decorative treatments. Also, they should be non-toxic to bats. When bats are present in a building, Scottish Natural Heritage must be consulted prior to embarking on treatment. (See 4.6 Repair of structural timbers).

3.2.11 MINOR REPAIRS TO SMALL AREAS OF INTERNAL PLASTER AND ASSOCIATED REDECORATION

New plaster should be carefully matched in mix and finish to the old (see 4.18 Repair of plain and decorative plasterwork for advice on repair of plaster). Internal decoration of plaster finishes to solid walls should never be undertaken using plastic (emulsion) paint as this will form an impervious skin which will inhibit the natural breathing process and be difficult to remove without damage - especially from ornamental cornices.

3.2.12 MINOR GLAZING REPAIRS

These include: replacement of individual broken panes (or in the case of leaded windows where feasible and appropriate, their retention by fitting additional cames); support of deformed leaded panels; removal of organic growth; etc. Broken glass should be replaced with glass of a matching type. Where glass is of historic importance, even minor works should be entrusted to a specialist conservator of glass (see 4.17 Repair of glass for more detailed advice on glazing repairs).

3.2.13 REGULAR PAINTING OF EXTERNAL WOODWORK

The protective coating to external timber elements should be regularly maintained using a breathable system if possible. Historically unpainted timber work should not be painted, but should be treated with a colourless penetrating preservation (not varnish). The use of a lead-based paint may be deemed appropriate for historic authenticity, but care must be taken not to contravene health and safety requirements. Associated fittings, such as door and window hinges, should also be properly maintained.

4

METHODS OF REPAIR

4.1 WORKS TO SECURE GENERAL STRUCTURAL STABILITY

4.1.1 PRELIMINARY INVESTIGATION

Leaning walls, cracks in masonry, etc. may be symptoms of foundation settlement or other structural movement of long standing which may have now stabilised. Before any action is taken, therefore, it is necessary to understand the building structure and monitor the situation over a period of time in order to determine whether or not movement is continuing and if it is, whether or not it is of sufficient seriousness to warrant action being taken. Monitoring should, wherever possible, be in excess of one year in order to take account of any ordinary seasonal variations in movement.

Specialist structural engineering advice is required on the need for monitoring and for any subsequent repairs. An engineer experienced in dealing with historic buildings should be chosen. It should also be noted in the context of work of this nature that Codes of Practice, Building Regulations, and current British Standards are not necessarily applicable.

Distortion of a building by settlement, here caused by mining subsidence, may be of long standing, and monitoring may be needed before it can be decided what structural repairs are required.

Where repairs are required, either in order to deal with defects caused by past movement which has now ceased, or where movement is still active, the aim should be wherever possible to stabilise and strengthen in situ, unless distortion or weakening of the structure is so far advanced that partial dismantling and rebuilding are unavoidable. In the latter case, the work should be preceded by a full drawn and photographic record in order to ensure accurate rebuilding. Components of the building should be numbered to correspond with numbers on drawings.

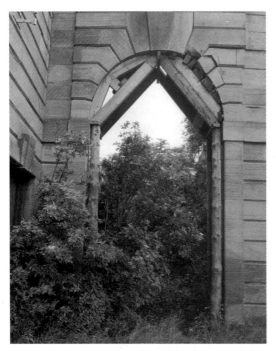

4.1.2 STABILISATION OF FOUNDATIONS

Shallow foundations on shrinkable clays can be affected by cyclical expansion and contraction of the clay around the periphery of a building, causing differential settlement. This may be affected by the presence of trees, particularly in areas of friable clay. It may be possible to stabilise the water level in the soil by providing a French drain falling to soakaways or to a nearby watercourse, if available; however, changes in ground conditions brought about by the introduction of drainage may themselves have undesirable effects, so engineering advice should always be obtained. If movement has already seriously affected the structure, however, it may be necessary to consider more radical measures such as underpinning the foundation below the level at which saturation takes place. Partial or intermittent underpinning should be avoided, as this is likely to settle differentially.

Another possible cause of foundation failure is ground settlement due to the collapse of subterrannean cavities or the compression of soft fill in ditches, pits etc., from previous human activity on or beneath a site.

Subsidence due to new mining is less likely to occur than in the past and adequate notice should have been given by the mining operator so that appropriate measures, such as the installation of a reinforced concrete raft, may be taken in advance and at his expense.

Because of the risks posed to the archeological record within the ground, such works will often require supervision by an archaeologist. Advice on this should be obtained from Historic Scotland.

Differential settlement has led to serious structural cracking and contributed to the dereliction of the building. (photo: I. Maxwell)

4.1.3   REPAIR OF LEANING WALLS

Foundations affected by differential settlement of the ground at the periphery of a building may cause walls to lean outwards, possibly with associated cracking at the corners of openings, pulling of floor beams and roof trusses from their bearing etc. Each case will require careful analysis before a decision is made on a method of repair. Where serious failure has occurred, methods of repair under consideration could prove to amount to total rebuilding, perhaps incorporating strengthening. Emphasis should be on doing the minimum possible that will ensure the safety of the structure.

In exceptional circumstances, where a wall is in danger of collapse, one possible method of repair might be the introduction of a reinforced concrete wall-top beam returned at either end linked to vertical reinforced posts, contained within the thickness of the wall. The posts

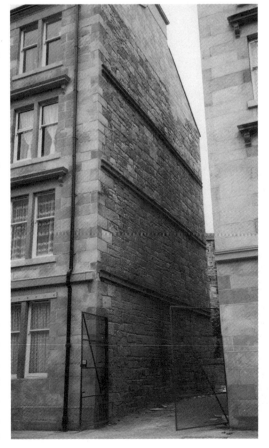

An apparently painstaking conservation project has been marred by the addition of structural steelwork to brace the gable, to replace the lintel on the ground floor window, and most likely steel is also concealed behind the "stone" banding course on the front.

would then be attached to horizontal members running back inside the building below floor level.

Care should, however, be taken over proposals for introducing rigid elements into relatively flexible structures, and the extent of their use in a particular case should be kept to the minimum required. In some circumstances a less drastic (and potentially reversible) type of repair may be made using steel plating in association with floor members, provided this can be achieved relatively unobtrusively. Alternatively, the insertion of tie-bars to fix one wall to its neighbour, or to connect walls to a restraining floor or roof structure may suffice.

The addition of conventional buttresses is normally to be avoided as these can settle independently, either falling away from the wall or pulling it over further by merely adding to the weight problem.

A masonry wall may be leaning because of foundation failure to an extent which threatens collapse. It may sometimes be possible to bring it back towards the vertical by forming a horizontal chase on the inside near the base, in order to form a 'hinge'. The foundation would then be re-formed as necessary and a framework and/or shoring erected on the outside of the wall. The wall would then be pulled back from behind by anchored steel cables, followed by the reinstatement of the chase.

In cases where walls lean for reasons other than foundation failure, eg. roof thrust, they may be anchored to floor beams or tie beams (following any necessary repairs to the roof structure) using straps and plates. Another method may be to install concealed tie rods across the width of the building or to major internal walls.

4.1.4 CRACKS AND UNSTABLE CORES

Cracks in walls caused by movement need to be dealt with in accordance with the degree of structural seriousness. It is necessary to determine whether failure is due to compression or tension, since treatment may involve a different approach or technique. Minor cracks may only require pointing. More serious ones may be repaired by stitching across the crack using material matching the wall construction, or by setting reinforced

Vegetation is contributing to forcing these ruined walls apart.

concrete stitchers or bonders behind the face work. Another method may be to insert non-ferrous metal ties in bed joints. Diagonal pinning across a crack with threaded stainless steel rods set in a resin grout may also be an appropriate method in some circumstances.

Pinning may also be used in conjunction with the grouting of rubble core filling where this has become loose and also where the face has bulged away from the core. The mix for the grout and method of application will vary according to the particular circumstances (eg. hand poured or gravity fed; pumped or pressure grouting etc., is generally not to be encouraged). The decision on

14

whether or not to carry out grouting should be carefully considered in terms of the effect it will have on the loading and flexibility of a wall.

It is particularly important that works involving the introduction of new components within the structure of a building are properly recorded and the information made accessible for future reference.

4.2 RECOVERING OF ROOFS

When a roof is stripped for recovering it is important that any necessary repairs to the roof structure are carried out at the same time (see 4.6 Repair of structural timbers),

together with other associated work at roof level, such as gutters, rhones, chimneystalks, parapets, gables and skews, dormers, rooflights etc. This averts the need for the later disturbance of recently laid roof finishes and makes the most economical use of scaffolding.

Unless there is good reason not to, roof coverings should be replaced on a like-for-like basis. Possible exceptions are discussed under the separate headings below.

4.2.1 SLATES, STONE SLATES, AND CLAY TILES INCLUDING PANTILES

Failure is usually caused by the corrosion of nails fixing slates or tiles to sarking or occasionally battens, the decay of the timber substrate, and the lamination or cracking of slates or tiles.

A Medieval trough-and-saddle stone roof and gutter have been coated and wrapped in a variety of substitute materials in an effort to keep water out. This is a problem with roofs of this age, but can really only be solved by careful pointing and regular maintenance.

When recovering, it is advisable to photograph the roof prior to stripping, to ensure that the existing details are properly followed.

Stripping should be carried out carefully to ensure that all sound existing slates or tiles remain undamaged so that they may be sorted according to type, size, and thickness and stored ready for re-use. When assessing existing slates or tiles for re-use, their likely further life should be carefully considered.

Unevenness of a roof surface is often part of the character of an old roof and unless it is likely to affect weathertightness, no attempt should be made to level up for the sake of creating an even surface.

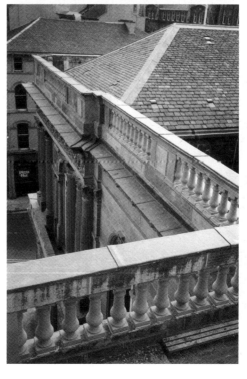

Ventilation of the roof space has been achieved by the reasonably unobtrusive introduction of proprietory units in the slating.

A breather sarking felt should be used and other means of ventilating the roof timbers should be introduced (eg. at the eaves) in order to reduce the risk of decay and fungal attack. Sarking felt should not be used where the underside of the slates or tiles is visible within a building, eg. barns and some other types of vernacular or early industrial buildings. Where mortar torching exists in such cases it should normally be kept and repaired or replaced, if

A sandstone slated roof gives much of the character of this historic building. Typically, Scottish slating is laid in diminishing courses.

necessary, particularly if it can be proved to be historic, but generally it is not recommended as part of good re-roofing practice.

Replacement sarking boards, battens or laths should be pre-treated against fungal attack. Existing boards should be renailed when reslating is carried out as their nails may have perished.

Reslating or retiling should be carried out using sound slates or tiles salvaged from the roof, with any deficiencies made up with sound secondhand materials, matching the existing ones in type, size, thickness, colour and texture. The selection of existing slates or tiles for re-use should be carried out with great care so as to ensure that they will have a significant life in relation to new material.

Substitute materials such as artificial slates made of fibre resin, artificial stone slates made of "reconstituted stone", concrete tiles etc., are not acceptable. Hand-made clay tiles should not be replaced with machine-made ones, nor pantiles with plain tiles.

If the existing slates or tiles are themselves an inappropriate earlier replacement, eg. Welsh slates introduced in the nineteenth century as a replacement for Ballachulish

Typical Scottish slating, laid in diminishing courses. Note the access ladder to enable the chimney to be maintained.

or other natural Scotch slate, it may be appropriate to restore the original material, provided that accurate evidence of its previous use survives and the existing material is of a type or condition that merits replacement.

The use of material cannibalised from other old buildings should be generally avoided wherever possible. New stone slates, natural slate such as Westmorland and hand-made tiles can usually be obtained and there is a need to encourage production.

It is preferable in some cases that sound old slates are laid together on visible slopes, with new ones kept for less prominent slopes and inner slopes of valleys etc. In all cases it is important to maintain the existing colour and texture of the roofs by mixing slates judiciously.

When using new stone slates etc., hand dressing will often be necessary to ensure good bedding, and to remove the mechanical appearance of machine-finished sides and tails.

Slates and stone slates, with the occasional exception of Welsh slates since the late eighteenth century, have almost always been laid in courses diminishing in size from the eaves to the ridge, and this should be carefully matched in recovering. When stripping, care should be taken to sort and stack the courses.

Fixing nails for slates and tiles should preferably be stout copper. Stainless steel nails are a possible alternative but it should be noted that they may be difficult to remove when repairs are necessary. Only nails with large-diameter shanks should be considered, otherwise they will tend to cut through the slate in time. Galvanised, plated, or plain steel nails should not be used. Where oak pegs or cast-iron pins have been used for slates, stone slates, or tiles on internally exposed roofs of barns etc., they should be replaced to match. Oak pegs should be treated, following shaping, against pest and fungal attack.

Details on roofs, such as ridge and hip covering, eaves, verges, valleys etc., will vary according to the roof covering, the building type and its period, regional variations etc. They should be replaced in their existing form, except where inappropriate and unsympathetic earlier changes have been made, in which case they should preferably be reinstated in their original form, provided there is sufficient evidence for this.

Some components are particularly valuable, eg. ornamental ridge or hip coverings of clay, lead, or iron, often with finials at the ends, or stone and slate ridges of various kinds. Existing sections are very often capable of re-use, but if beyond repair they should be carefully re-made in a matching material and design.

Good practice in reslating a roof with lead hips. Duckboards will facilitate future maintenance. (photo: I. Maxwell)

Lead watergates (or occasionally soakers) and flashings should be provided at abutments of roofs with gables, skews, chimneystalks etc., although in some cases other more locally traditional details should be retained where they exist, eg. a mortar fillet, possibly provided with a lead watergate below. Lead should be fixed into joints to avoid the raggling of masonry wherever possible.

4.2.2   METAL ROOF COVERINGS

Lead

Where very old lead survives on roofs it should be regarded as a valuable part of the fabric of the building and wherever possible should be kept and repaired rather than replaced. Such work may involve refixing slipped sheets, possibly replacing some which are worn out, reforming details of rolls, flashings etc., and repairing splits and holes with lead-welded patches, including the replacement by lead welding of ineffective soldered repairs. Strict fire precautions should be observed during the carrying out of such work.

Repair, rather than complete replacement, may be appropriate for later lead roofs. If, however, inherent faults exist in a lead roof or gutter linings such as oversized or overfixed sheets leading to damage caused by thermal movement, insufficient fixing causing slipping, poorly detailed drips, splash laps or rolls etc., which have been a constant source of trouble necessitating regular repair, then complete replacement will be required. Names and dates cast into the sheets of an old roof or old graffiti may be of interest and worth saving. If they cannot be retained in situ, they should be kept safely within the building.

Good modern practice in lead work

New leadwork should be specified correctly in respect of sizes of sheet and thickness, falls, and details of joints and fixings. The thickness of lead for pitched roofs, flat roofs, gutter linings, and ridge cappings should not be less than Code 7 or 8; for watergates,

Plaques on lead roofs can become of historic interest, as lead can last well over 100 years, and should be retained. When the lead is replaced the plaque should be kept within the building.

vertical cladding and hip flashings, Code 6; for cover flashings and for soakers, Code 5. Compliance with current standards for sheet sizes will often entail reforming the substrate to achieve adequate falls. Cast lead is normally to be preferred when replacing historic material.

Occasionally it may be proposed that a timber gutter base be replaced with concrete. This should normally be avoided, and should only be considered as a possibility where the timber is in need of major renewal due to rot, or where major reconstruction of the gutter is needed in order to provide correct falls, sheet sizes etc. Otherwise the existing construction should be kept and repaired as necessary. If concrete is decided upon it must be possible to isolate fully any structural timbers from it by an air gap of at least 25mm on three sides to prevent the development of rot. Merely wrapping timbers in polythene, etc. is not sufficient. Expansion joints should be provided in the concrete on the line of each drip.

Corrosion caused by condensation on the underside of lead on roofs has become a problem of increasing concern. It is frequently found where the internal environment of a building has been changed by the installation of central heating or intermittent systems of heating and where there is inadequate general ventilation. This situation is worsened when associated with leadwork of non-traditional design which does not allow ventilation to the underside of the lead, thereby preventing condensation from evaporating and thus accelerating corrosion.

While ventilation of the underside of lead roof coverings to the external air is essential, the system, known as a "ventilated warm roof", is complicated and of doubtful relevance to historic building repair work. Its extra thickness can make detailing at verges and abutments awkward, or be visually obtrusive where there are no parapets.

Wherever traditional construction has proved to be successful the presumption should usually be in favour of its being repeated when replacement of the covering is necessary, even though this may make difficult the provision of modern comforts such as insulation. Where buildings are only heated intermittently (eg. many churches), insulation will in any case be of little benefit (see 5.1 Heating and Ventilation).

In some cases, where a roof which was originally lead clad may have been recovered at a later date with another material, usually for cheapness, it may be appropriate to revert to lead.

Stainless steel

In cases where there has been a persistent history of the theft of lead from a roof and it can be shown that all reasonable security measures have been tried and have failed, then use of an alternative material may be considered acceptable, subject to full approval. It should be noted however, that where lead is a prominent feature of the design and appearance of a building, it is unlikely that any other material would be acceptable.

Where it is agreed that an alternative material to lead may be used, dull-finished stainless steel may be acceptable provided that a roof is hidden by parapets etc. Although the detailing of stainless steel is different from lead, similar sheet widths should be chosen for the sake of appearance. Due to the difficult workability of stainless steel it may be necessary to use lead for some complicated junctions, flashings etc., and possibly also to retain lead for gutters.

Where a roof is visible from below, terne-coated stainless steel might be considered.

Copper

In the past copper was sometimes introduced as a replacement for lead, and although the problem of pitch does not arise, it is usually preferable - when the copper has reached the end of its life - to reinstate lead on the grounds that it is historically and visually appropriate, subject to the roof being capable of bearing its weight.

Thatching in progress: applying rye straw in straight lines from eaves to ridge over a turf undercloak.

When copper was the original material, however, it is often important to the design intention, and when replacement is necessary it should be on a like-for-like basis.

Detailed specifications for copper roofing should ensure that bay sizes, weight, and fixing details are correct so as to minimise the risk of damage by wind lift, thermal movement, and condensation.

4.2.3 THATCH

When re-thatching, it is important to maintain regional characteristics of material and of general form and detail. The materials most commonly in use today are long straw, combed wheat reed, water reed, marram grass, heather, rushes, oat straw, barley straw, broom and turf, some in the form of clay thatch. Turf or concrete can be used for ridges when treated independently of the main roof surface. There may sometimes be reasons for reinstating thatch on a building that was originally thatched but was later re-roofed with another material.

Scottish thatched roofs can be divided into 2 main groups:

● those where the thatching material is carried over the ridge as an uninterrupted surface and,

● those where the ridge is treated separately from the main roof surface.

Reed thatch roof with concrete ridge: note also modern services installation within a thatched house.

Within these main groups are a multitude of regional and local variations, particularly on vernacular roofs. "Polite" thatched roofs mainly follow English practices. In order to ensure that such regional features are not lost when re-thatching, an experienced thatcher should be employed who works in accordance with local tradition. Old photographs etc., may be consulted in order to ensure accurate reinstatement of original features.

Complete stripping is often needed but where possible only defective thatch should be removed, to a sound base. Sometimes original layers may survive below, possibly retaining valuable historical evidence such as smoke-blackened thatch and timbers in domestic roofs, surviving from the time before a chimneystalk was inserted. Care should be taken to ensure that such features remain undisturbed. Smoke-blackened thatch is usually very fragile. Some thatched roofs are supported on straw mat and/or straw, heather, coir or even wire ropes. These features should be retained or reinstated during re-thatching.

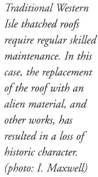

Traditional Western Isle thatched roofs require regular skilled maintenance. In this case, the replacement of the roof with an alien material, and other works, has resulted in a loss of historic character. (photo: I. Maxwell)

Felt underlay or polythene sheeting should not be used for thatched roofs as it will inhibit drying out.

If anti-fire devices are introduced for thatch, they should be visually acceptable.

Rooflights and dormers in Scottish vernacular thatched roofs are extremely simple in appearance. When considering the introduction of new rooflights or dormers check photographic evidence for acceptable solutions in the area or region.

4.2.4 SHINGLES

Shingles were used on early Scottish buildings, for example, the Canongate Tolbooth in Edinburgh.

Shingles are traditionally of cleft oak. If the materials are properly selected and fixed, a shingle roof should have a life of up to seventy years. Sawn cedar shingles are not usually an acceptable alternative, being larger and full and flat in appearance. If oak cannot be obtained, cleft sweet chestnut shingles (available from France) are acceptable, being of the correct size and after weathering, a reasonable match in appearance and texture. As they are made from young trees, however, both edges are likely to contain sapwood, and so preservative treatment by pressure impregnation is necessary. Replacement shingles should not be lighter in weight than the original ones.

As shingles need adequate ventilation underneath, felt underlay should not be used, except for particularly exposed situations where a breather felt is advisable.

If pre-drilled to prevent splitting, shingles may be fixed by stout copper nails; alternatively, two thin stainless steel nails may be used without pre-drilling. Galvanised steel nails should not be used.

Where there is a danger of attack by woodpeckers, a strip of zinc may be inserted behind each course of shingles.

4.2.5 ASPHALT

Recovering in asphalt is acceptable where this is the original material. The work should be carried out in accordance with the best current practice. Where, however, asphalt has earlier been laid on a timber roof which was originally covered with lead, then lead should be reinstated when the asphalt has reached the end of its life.

3-ply bituminous felt was used on Scottish roofs from the 1760s. Older examples normally have a tarred finish dusted with ashes externally. However re-felting is not generally recommended except for vernacular buildings, due to shortness of life.

4.2.6 DORMERS AND SKYLIGHTS

Dormers vary in form from the simple "cat-slide" type clad with slate or tile, to architecturally important features with pediments of stone or moulded timber, covered with lead, and with lead cheeks. All details should be carefully followed in repairs. Any lost features of significance, or unsympathetic alterations, should be made good provided sufficiently accurate evidence exists, either from adjacent dormers or from old photographs and drawings, eg. the lead covering a pediment may later have been inappropriately replaced, or the astragals of windows may have been lost.

Skylights also vary widely in size and degree of elaboration, depending on the building type and whether or not they are intended to be significant elements of the design, either when seen externally, or from an important internal space such as a staircase. When repairs are carried out, materials, usually timber or iron, and details of mouldings, astragals etc., should be carefully matched. Although it may sometimes be necessary to improve weathertightness by modifying flashings etc., this should be done unobtrusively. Old glass, including coloured or patterned glass sometimes found in nineteenth-century skylights, should always be carefully retained during repairs.

Plain, iron-framed skylights set below the plane of the roof should not as a rule be replaced with a modern type with different details. Exceptions may only possibly be considered where a skylight is completely hidden from external view on inner slopes etc., and where it is not visible from important internal spaces. Such an alteration could require statutory consent. Where modern roof-lights are used, the fixing and flashing details should be modified so that the outer surface of the light is below the plane of the roof.

4.3   RENEWAL OF RAINWATER GOODS

Cracked or broken cast-iron rhones and rhonepipes should be replaced in matching material and section, eg. half-round, box, or ogee gutters, and round or rectangular section downpipes etc. In the case of some complicated sections it may be feasible and economical to repair the existing ones by welding. Substitute materials such as pvc or extruded aluminium are generally not acceptable, although coloured cast aluminium may be considered in some cases. Sound existing lengths of cast iron should be reused after de-rusting. Special castings may be needed for some lengths if unobtainable from stock. If an existing system is functionally deficient in certain locations, eg. undersized rhones or pipes, unable to cope with heavy rain, then it may be necessary to fit larger components, but they should be of the same design and not so much larger as significantly to affect the appearance of the building. A drainage problem may be overcome by an extra downpipe, the location of which should be approved.

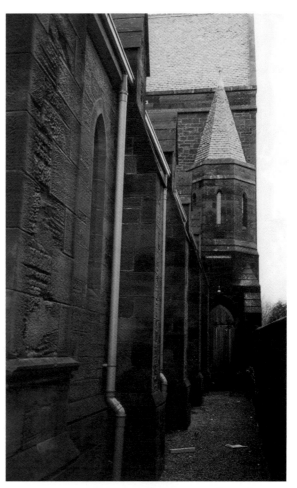

Defective rhone pipes have been replaced but unfortunately in all too conspicuous PVC.

Rhonepipes should be fitted on spacers or holder-batts far enough from the wall that if a leak should occur water will run down the back of the pipe and not down the wall. Pipes should also be located clear of internal corners or re-entrant angles where their failure can often go undetected. This will also allow a free flow of air round the pipe to inhibit the development of rust and permit repainting of the back without contaminating the adjacent wall face. Fixings should also allow for ease of dismantling.

Where there are sensitive internal features, such as wall paintings, it may be prudent to consider re-siting rhonepipes well away from them.

Lead downpipes, rainwater heads, and gutters should, wherever possible, be overhauled by reforming sagged or dented sections and repairing splits by lead welding, not soldering. When sections are beyond repair they should be replaced in a matching weight of lead to the same design. Iron fixings should not be used.

In circumstances where there is persistent theft or vandalism, consideration may be given to the replacement of the lowest or most accessible sections of lead downpipes in a substitute material such as cast iron or, possibly terne-coated stainless steel.

Rainwater heads should be fitted with overflows where these do not already exist and where they would not interfere with a fine design. Water spouts on high roofs should be of sufficient projection to prevent water from falling against the building as far as is practical.

Wooden gutters, chutes, or downpipes are rare and should be repaired in matching timber to the same design. Elm is a traditional material for gutters, as it swells rapidly when wet and prevents leakage.

Where appropriate, stone gutters may be lined with lead if proper jointing is feasible. If it is not possible to achieve correct sheet lengths by other means, the use of patent expansion jointing systems may be acceptable.

4.4   REPAIR OR INSTALLATION OF SURFACE WATER DRAINAGE

Duff House: an open drainage channel revealed around the base of the walls of an 18th Century mansion.
(photo: I. Maxwell)

The installation of a French drain around the perimeter of a church is usually the most sensitive method of disposing of surface water, but great care must be taken where burials occur and excavations for such work should always be monitored by an archaeologist.

Rhonepipes should discharge over gullies (not back-inlet gullies; see 3.2.5), which should be connected to drains running, if possible, to a nearby watercourse or to main drains. If these are not available, properly designed soakaways should be constructed at a distance from the building. Catch pits and rodding eyes should be incorporated in the system.

It is not satisfactory for a rhonepipe to discharge into a perimeter drainage channel as the concentration of water on one spot is likely to wash away mortar from joints in the channel and cause seepage of water into foundations and rising damp in the wall.

Perimeter drainage channels are common around churches, either at ground level or sunk into a 'dry area', and having surfaces of brick, tile or stone. Such channels are not always satisfactory, as the surface is liable to settle and crack away from the wall, letting water into the foundations. Where this is occuring, the channel should be removed and another system installed, eg. a French drain connected to a watercourse or a soakaway. This may not be possible, however, where there are shallow foundations. It should also be noted that a French drain must be correctly installed and properly maintained otherwise there is a risk that it may block and allow water to collect against the foundations. It is preferable to fill the trench to the top with stones or gravel. The archeological implications of such work due to the likely presence of graves and burials should always be taken into account in the case of churches. There is also the risk of disturbing highly valuable evidence of the development of the church and the relationship between internal and external stratification.

4.5 PREVENTION OF RISING DAMP AND ASSOCIATED PROBLEMS

4.5.1 WALLS

Only when rising damp is causing significant deterioration, particularly if salts are also present, will it usually be necessary to take measures to prevent it. Particular care should, however, be taken to ensure that damp is kept away from built-in timbers.

Before any measures are taken the problem should be analysed in order to identify the cause properly. In the first instance professional advice should be obtained, rather than that of a specialist contractor. Dampness may occur in walls because of factors other than rising damp caused by moisture in the ground, eg. leaking rhones, defective drains, open joints or cracks in walls, moisture trapped behind hard renders, burst plumbing, condensation due to inadequate ventilation etc. If, however, rising damp is diagnosed, the measures taken to reduce it will vary according to particular conditions.

Where the external ground level is higher than the floor level, causing moisture to penetrate horizontally through the wall, the possibility of regrading the ground level should first be investigated. If this is not feasible, then an open trench or "dry area" may be formed with a French drain at its base.

Provided the foundations are not too shallow, this method may also be used when the external ground level is not higher than floor level but where a high water table is causing rising damp. In these circumstances, however, a more economical solution is to install a simple French drain without a "dry area". The drain should be kept at least 200mm from a foundation base. Before embarking on excavation adjacent to an historic building, however, archeological advice should be obtained and, where appropriate, supervision and recording by a specialist should be arranged.

Where it is not feasible to provide perimeter drainage, other methods which may be considered are:

● the insertion of a damp-proof membrane by cutting a slot in short lengths across the full width of the wall and inserting a strip of material such as lead, lead-cored bitumen felt, copper, heavy-gauge polythene, etc. Each length of membrane must have an adequate lap over or below its neighbour. This method is restricted, however, to walls of regular-coursed masonry, of a thickness not too great for the cutting machine, and the membrane must be inserted below the level of a timber ground floor;

Salt crystallisation damage and build up of algae on stonework.

● the formation of a damp-proof barrier by impregnating the masonry with a chemical solution. This method is unlikely to be effective when walls have rubble cores containing voids, unless these can be effectively consolidated prior to impregnation, or where walls are more than 600mm thick.

Any works to install a damp-proof membrane must be carefully considered and care taken not to disfigure the face of the building by cutting or drilling into ashlar masonry.

Measures such as the application of an impervious render or other waterproofed surface on the inside face should not be used, as they will only serve to trap moisture behind them and drive it further up the wall to emerge at a higher level.

4.5.2   FLOORS

A good thickness of hand-packed hardcore blinded off with fine material will provide a satisfactory base for bedding flagstones that will reduce rising dampness and not drive moisture elsewhere. Where rising damp and resultant salt deposits are significantly damaging a tiled or flagged ground floor, the insertion of a damp-proof membrane under the floor should only be considered where it is not possible significantly to improve the situation by installing perimeter drainage outside the building. Another method may be to form a gap between the edge of the floor and the wall to encourage evaporation of moisture. If such methods are not feasible and it is agreed that a membrane is needed, a damp-proofing system should be installed within the walls at the same time as the installation of the floor membrane, otherwise damp will be driven up the wall.

Membranes may be installed below the plates of timber ground floor constructions when damp conditions exist. Voids below timber floors must be properly ventilated so that moisture may disperse.

In any disturbance of historic floors and their substrates, archeological advice should be obtained and followed.

4.6   REPAIR OF STRUCTURAL TIMBERS
(Roof structures, wall frames, floor beams etc.).
4.6.1   FUNGAL ATTACK

Outbreaks of fungal attack in timber (wet and dry rot) should be dealt with by identifying and remedying the cause; treatment with even the most potent fungicide will be ineffective if the source of moisture is not stopped (eg. leaking gutters and downpipes, blocked parapet and valley gutters, blocked drains etc.) and proper permanent ventilation introduced to floor voids, roof spaces, partition studding etc.

A fungicide-containing barrier may need to be considered to prevent the spread of the fungus for as long as it takes for the affected part of the structure to dry out. The fungus will die off completely in dry conditions (ie. below 20% moisture content) within about 12 months, although where timbers are embedded in thick masonry it may take longer. During this time environmental conditions must be regularly and frequently monitored and controlled. It is only necessary to cut out and replace members or parts of members which are directly infected or structurally weakened by the fungus. The often destructive results of standard methods of eradication can thus be avoided.

Where fungal attack is discovered, particularly dry rot, measures should be taken against it immediately. Failure to do so in warm and damp conditions will risk it spreading rapidly. Removal of water source and provision of ventilation are the most important immediate actions, followed by the removal of any impervious finishes which prevent moisture dispersal. Fungicides should be non-toxic to users of the building and all chemical treatments should be used strictly in accordance with Health and Safety recommendations.

4.6.2 INSECT ATTACK

Common furniture beetle can cause considerable structural damage in a building. Some limited defrassing may be necessary in order to determine the severity of the attack and the extent to which the strength of a member has been impaired. This should be carried out with great care and generally avoided as it may expose sound timber to further infestation. In the case of moulded work it should be avoided in favour of treating and conserving the weakened timber surface. A drawn record should be made of the original profiles for future reference.

Before chemical timber treatment against wood-boring insects is considered it should be noted that such treatment is essentially a device to buy time: it is likely to provide protection for approximately five years.

It is not necessarily appropriate to carry out chemical treatment simply as a "precaution": there should be clear evidence of need. Selective rather than wholesale treatment is always preferable.

Insecticide where used should be applied to all accessible surfaces by spray, brush, or injection as appropriate, with particular attention to joints, shakes, and end grain. If preservative fluids are used they should only be of a water-based and colourless type and care should be taken to ensure that historic surfaces and decorative treatments are not damaged. The manufacturers' safety precautions should be scrupulously followed to avoid any health risk to users of the building.

Where bats are inhabiting a building, treatments should be non-toxic to them. Under the Wildlife and Countryside Act 1981 there is an obligation on owners of such buildings to consult Scottish Natural Heritage before any work is carried out.

4.6.3 REPAIRS

As much of the original timber as possible has been retained, splicing in new only where it has been irrevocably weakened by woodworm infestation etc. Note the use of pegs bolting new timber to old in the rafter sections.

Wherever possible, repairs to structural timbers should be carried out in timber using traditional carpentry methods, retaining all sound existing material, and replacing only what is necessary in order to restore structural integrity. Badly decayed or seriously split members or parts of members should be carefully cut away and new sections spliced in, using timber of the same species and scantling as the original. Oak used in repairs should preferably be new, after a sufficient laying-down period which may take years rather than months. The use of oak cannibalised from old buildings should be avoided.

If old timbers are found to have painted decoration which may be of interest, the advice of a specialist conservator and Historic Scotland should be sought.

The use of a steel flitch as part of an open "in situ" repair to the end of a floor beam. (photo: A. Cruden)

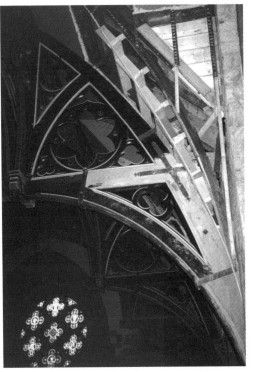

Following an outbreak of dry rot, this Victorian hammer beam roof truss has unfortunately been repaired with epoxy resin rather than by splicing in new timber.

The repair of a weakened roof structure may sometimes be achieved by reinstating a missing member such as a brace or strut, or by making good a member cut through during alterations, eg. a severed collar of a truss or a purlin severed when an attic was formed or a dormer window inserted.

Although the carrying out of repairs by carpentry methods is usually to be preferred, these may sometimes involve undue disturbance of an historic structure. It may then be necessary to consider other methods, provided they are visually acceptable, eg. a steel flitch or bolted plates or angles. Another method which may occasionally be appropriate is the use of carbon fibre reinforcement rods to carry out the in situ strengthening of a decayed structural member. After the rods are inserted they may be secured in place with resin and their ends concealed with a plug of matching timber. Care must be taken by this method not to overstrengthen the joint and so prevent any movement being taken up.

In some cases strengthening may be achieved by the insertion of additional timber members alongside existing ones, such as the duplication of rafters or perhaps the insertion of an intermediate truss where a roof is not exposed internally. Care should be taken however, not to introduce too many changes in load patterns, as this can trigger off new problems.

The use of resins in timber repairs should only be considered with great care and only normally where carpentry methods are impracticable. They should not be used where timbers are exposed to external conditions. On no account should they be looked upon as an "easy option". In cases where it is agreed that their use is appropriate, the work should always be carried out by a joiner experienced in the repair of historic buildings and with an understanding of how they function structurally.

In some circumstances, epoxy resins may enable in situ repairs to be carried out involving minimal loss of historic fabric, eg. where there are voids formed by insect attack behind an original moulded or carved face of a member which it is of prime importance to preserve. In such conditions, wood consolidants may also be considered to help conserve friable carved work.

The cleaning of historic timber elements, eg. ceilings, should be considered only with extreme caution and in consultation with a specialist conservator. Any technique that disturbs or removes the original sawn, planed or adzed finish should be avoided. Even when cleaning is carefully carried out there is a risk of removing surviving painted decoration or other evidence of a building's history.

4.7   REPAIR OF STONEWORK

Where dirt deposits on stonework or brickwork are of a kind that is actually causing damage, eg. blistering sulphate skins or where they are of such thickness that it is not possible to decide properly on the scope of necessary repairs, then their removal may be desirable. Very careful cleaning by a specialist conservator is usually an essential preliminary to conservation work on valuable carved work etc. Exceptionally, there may be aesthetic reasons for stone cleaning. Unless there are sound practical reasons or conservation grounds for doing so, the cleaning of masonry is best avoided because of the damage which may be caused, and

The cleaning of this building for cosmetic reasons has only served to exacerbate the problem of its advanced stone decay.

listed building consent may be required. If it is decided that cleaning is necessary, the method to be used will depend on the nature of the soiling and the type of stone or brick. Some methods, eg. pressure grit-blasting, should be avoided in almost all circumstances. When a technique, or if appropriate, a combination of techniques, has been selected and agreed, a sample of cleaning should be approved by the architect before work proceeds. It must be recognised that any cleaning - particularly of sandstone - causes a certain amount of damage, and decisions on whether or not to clean must be made on a damage limitation basis which balances anticipated benefits against the likely extent of damage.

It is essential that both the geophysical properties of the stone and the causes of damage and decay are first carefully investigated and identified in order that, where possible, their effect may be eliminated or reduced, and decisions on the scope and methods of repair may be correctly related to them.

The expansion of rusting window ferramenta causing stonework to spall. The ends of the ferramenta should be tipped with a suitable non-ferrous metal and the stone repaired by piecing-in.

Typical problems are: repeated crystallisation of salts within the pores or on the surface of the stone, acidic dry deposition and rainfall, run-off from lichens, splitting due to the freezing of water in pockets or crevices, the weathering out of soft clay or sandy beds, contour-scaling of sandstone, wrongly bedded stonework, serious rising damp, decay caused by insufficient protection of surfaces due to damaged drip-moulds, copings, etc., leaking rhones or rhonepipes, spalling caused by expansion of rusting iron cramps or window ferramenta, sandstone decayed by run-off from limestone, defective pointing, inappropriate or aggressively executed cleaning, stone decay caused by hard, cement-rich mortars for pointing, areas of surface spalling due to trapped moisture caused by inappropriate attempts to preserve the stone, such as the application of silicone, linseed oil, etc., damage by masonry bees (see 4.13 Repair of earth walls).

Stones should only be replaced where they have lost their structural integrity because of deep erosion, or serious fracture or spalling, or where weatherings are no longer performing the function of throwing water

The complete replacement of original tracery and mullions of a 19th century window, accurately reproducing original detailing.

clear of surfaces below. If erosion or spalling is only superficial it should be accepted, and loose, water-holding material lightly and carefully brushed off. The redressing or dressing-back of surfaces is not acceptable in most cases.

Decisions on the extent of replacement should, however, also consider the interpretation and context of the structure. In some cases conserving as much as possible of the existing fabric may prompt the retention of stones that might otherwise be regarded as defective. Practical considerations should also be taken into account. Difficulty of access and the cost of scaffolding, eg. when working on towers, clerestories etc., may make it cost effective to carry out all work that is thought likely to be necessary for, say, the next 25 years.

The scope of replacement should be agreed as far as possible from the ground and from ladders etc., prior to the preparation of a specification and schedule. The schedule should include marked-up photocopies of sufficiently detailed photographs, or be shown on drawings. Areas for repointing, any cracks to be stitched, or zones to be grouted etc., should also be indicated.

When scaffolding has been erected (which should have plastic pole end caps for the protection of the stone), the stonework should be inspected in detail in order that the work may be agreed on a stone-by-stone basis and the schedule confirmed or amended as necessary. Stones should be marked on the building to correspond with those marked on photocopies or drawings. For the repair of window tracery, the photocopies or drawings should differentiate between stones which require indents, those which need to be cut out to the glass line only, and those needing replacement in full depth (rarely necessary).

Where it is agreed that a feature needs to be dismantled and rebuilt, such as a finial, parapet, cupola etc., all stones should be numbered, with corresponding numbers shown on a detailed drawing in order to ensure accurate reinstatement. If it is agreed that

A stone steeple with failing mortar is reconstructed on a stainless steel armature to ensure its stability in a windswept location.

moulded or carved work needs to be replaced (see below), the details of the original should be matched by measuring a sheltered uneroded section, or by referring to reliable documentation. Detailed drawings should be approved in advance. Replacement stones should match the original in size, shape, colour, texture, qualities of durability, and surface finish, eg. rubble for rubble and ashlar for ashlar; any tooling must be carefully carried out to match a sheltered example of the original. It is also important to ensure that bed joints are correctly tooled.

Ideally, stone should come from the same quarry as the original, provided the durability of the currently available stone is considered adequate and it can be obtained in sufficient depth of bed. If this is impossible, a matching, geologically compatible stone should be obtained. In general, cast stone or reconstituted stone is inappropriate as it has different weathering qualities from natural stone. Only in exceptional circumstances should reconstituted stone or plastic repair be considered, for example where the replacement of whole stones is particularly onerous, eg. cornices. Even then, the original stone dust should be reused if possible.

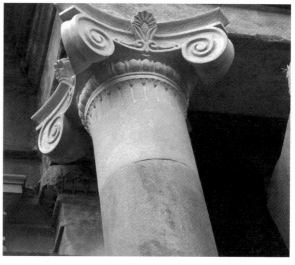

A fair attempt at replacing an Ionic capital in natural stone, though the carving lacks depth.

Generally, except when dealing with carved or moulded work or with window tracery, the use of small stone indents should be avoided, so that original joint-lines are respected. Another possible exception may be where relatively small spalls have occurred due to rusting iron cramps. After the removal of the cramp and its replacement in stainless steel or phosphor bronze, the stone may be repaired with a small indent, unobtrusively rubbed-in, or tooled to match its parent stone. Such indents must not cross existing joint-lines.

Replacement stones should normally be set to the original face-line, unless this could lead to accelerated weathering of surrounding stone or be too visually disruptive, in which case some compromise may be justified. Replacement stones should be correctly bedded - usually on their natural bedding plane, except for cornices, copings, string courses etc., which should be edge-bedded, and arch voussoirs, which should be bedded approximately parallel to the radius of the arch. In medieval buildings, however, such details were often cut to be laid on the bed, and this should only change if weathering would be considerably improved by doing so.

Replacement guilloche ornament, crudely executed. Even worse is the effort to sharpen up the original.

Carved work should, wherever possible, be conserved and consolidated rather than replaced, ie. an attempt should be made to hold back or slow down the rate of decay. It is likely that a comprehensive programme of repair will involve a combination of

A squared rubble wall into which new sandstone has been crudely inserted straight from the saw. The attempt at reproducing the tooling is creditable but deviates considerably from the original.

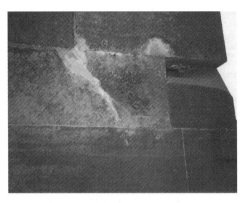

This characteristic spalling pattern in tightly-bedded ashlar usually indicates that the dressed stone is secured to the rubble core with iron cramps (one of which is visible), that are expanding with rust and pushing off the face stone.

conservation and consolidation in some areas and stone replacement in others. Prior to any work, the ornament should be recorded by photography, photogrammetry or drawings. Where carved work is a separate element of the building, for example statues or effigies, there may be a case for removal to a protected environment and replacement on the building with a replica.

Methods of conservation and consolidation which might be considered are as follows:

● plastic or special mortar repair. This should only be used sparingly, in the spirit of "dentistry", for the filling of relatively small cavities which might hold water. It should not be seen as an inexpensive alternative to necessary replacement. In fact, if properly carried out by a skilled mason/conservator, as it should be, it is rarely cheaper. Its principal merit is that it often allows for the retention of more of the original fabric than if stone were to be pieced-in, but it should never be used in lieu of essential structural repair;

● the holding of valuable fractured stone by stainless steel pins set in low viscosity epoxy resin;

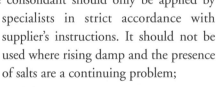

● prolonging the life of masonry attacked by salts by attempting to remove the salt with a poultice, a "sacrificial" render of lime and sand, or exceptionally, lime putty;

● consolidation of limestone by the "lime method" of repeated applications of limewater, the filling of cracks and small cavities with special repair mortar, and the provision of a sacrificial lime "shelter coat";

The face of this original ashlar has been aggressively tooled off, or dressed back, thus radically changing the appearance of the building.

● the use of alkoxy silane-based consolidants with the object of arresting the rapid loss of friable material from valuable stonework. It is claimed that this treatment achieves a deep penetration (over 20mm) which lines the pores of the stone, while allowing it to continue to "breathe". This method should only usually be considered however, where other measures are unlikely to be effective, or as "last-ditch" effort, largely because its long-term effects are as yet unknown. It is also expensive. The advice of an expert stone conservator should first be obtained and the consolidant should only be applied by specialists in strict accordance with supplier's instructions. It should not be used where rising damp and the presence of salts are a continuing problem;

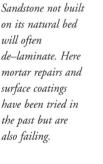

Sandstone not built on its natural bed will often de–laminate. Here mortar repairs and surface coatings have been tried in the past but are also failing.

● the provision of lead flashings to prolong the life of decayed projecting features such as cornices, but only where this can be achieved unobtrusively.

For important carved work, the carrying out of any of the above measures should

be preceded by the preparation of a full drawn and photographic record for future reference, when replacement may ultimately become unavoidable, before the stage when erosion is such that a carving loses its architectural and artistic value. The point at which consideration needs to be given to the removal of the original work and to placing it under cover for protection - replacing it with a copy - is not usually easy to determine. The advice of a specialist conservator and of Historic Scotland should be obtained.

In cases where a type of stone is of very poor weathering quality, either inherently so or because of poor selection, and where long exposure, combined possibly with lack of maintenance, has resulted in an overall extremely severe degree of decay, it may be appropriate to consider harling or rendering, when the only alternative would be to completely reface or indent. Factors which will need to be taken into account are the architectural quality and character of the building, including whether the stone is ashlar or rubble (it is more appropriate for the latter) and the major effect harling or rendering would have on its appearance (listed building consent or scheduled monument consent would be required). Other considerations are whether or not the depth of decay in the stone is endangering the structure and whether or not the stone is capable of allowing harling or render properly to adhere to it. Where appropriate, specialist advice should be sought at an early stage. (See 4.12 Repair of external render and harling for advice on render and harling).

Altered almost out of recognition, a late classical building with severely eroding sandstone ashlar has been covered, irreversably with a proprietory PVA (poly vinyl acetate) coating.

The carved sandstone armorial panels are rapidly reaching the end of their lives. To stem further erosoion, treatment with silane may be the only option.

Trying to prolong the life of masonary by painting it is often a waste of effort, even using micro-porous systems. Stones must breathe and the escaping moisture will either be trapped and break down the stone or push off the pigment. The same can usually be said for stone sealants.

4.8   REPAIR OF BRICKWORK

Although stone is often throught of as characteristically Scottish, due to the geological richness of the country, the use of brick in Scotland dates from at least the mid 17th century (eg. Glamis Ice House). It can therefore legitimately be considered a traditional material, though most examples are more recent.

Many of the considerations which apply to the repair of stonework also apply to brickwork, and again the causes of decay should first be identified and wherever possible remedial measures taken to prevent or reduce further damage.

As with stonework, damage is most frequently the result of water penetration, so exposed features such as cornices, string courses, copings, plinth offsets etc. are likely to be most affected, particularly where formed of the soft bricks known as rubbers used in gauged work. Open joints and cracks will of course accentuate water penetration.

Rising damp often brings with it damage from salt crystallisation, and the softer types of brick are those most likely to be affected.

Templeton's carpet factory in Glasgow is a fine example of gauged brick and diaper work.

Where a wall is exposed on both sides (eg. a parapet) and is therefore more vulnerable to saturation, it is very likely that frost damage may occur. In some cases it may be advisable to consider protecting the inside face of a parapet, eg. with render, slate, or lead cladding.

Where individual defective bricks are found in an otherwise sound area of wall this is often the result of poor firing or because of "foreign" material in the clay.

The number of bricks that are sufficiently decayed to be in need of replacement should be accurately identified. Only bricks that are beyond retention on structural grounds should be renewed. This is particularly important in the case of fine quality gauged work, repairs which should be recorded on marked-up drawings.

The method of cutting out should be chosen so as to cause the minimum of disturbance to surrounding sound bricks. In some cases, where an excessive degree of disturbance is likely to be caused, it may be necessary to use brick slips rather than full-depth bricks, but this method should be restricted to individual bricks or very small areas because of inherent structural weakness.

Replacement bricks should match the existing ones in dimensions, strength and durability, texture of finish, and colour. They should be laid in the same bond and width of joint. It is particularly important in achieving the latter to ensure that an exactly matching size of brick is selected. The appearance of a wall can be seriously impaired by different joint widths for areas of replacement brickwork.

In order to achieve a proper match it may be necessary to have new bricks specially fired, in which case the need to order sufficiently far in advance should be anticipated. Matching secondhand bricks may be available, although this source should be viewed with caution as it may entail damage to or loss of another historic building. Care should also be taken to ensure that secondhand bricks were not intended for internal use only and are therefore unable to withstand external weathering.

Where a wall or part of it is structurally unstable and rebuilding is unavoidable, a record should be made prior to dismantling to ensure an accurate reconstruction. This is especially the case where brickwork incorporates decorative patterns such as diaper work, or traces of original decorative treatments.

4.9   REPOINTING OF STONEWORK AND BRICKWORK

Repointing should only be undertaken where mortar has weathered out, leaving open or deeply recessed joints vulnerable to water penetration, or where the mortar is very soft or loose.

The comprehensive repointing of a building is rarely necessary. Those parts which are most exposed to the weather are most likely to be in need of attention, or areas affected by specific problems such as rising damp. Even in such cases, deterioration may not be uniform and sound old pointing should be left undisturbed. It is an essential part of the fabric and character of a building and its unnecessary removal is unacceptable.

Mortar should never be removed forcibly by the use of a mechanical disc cutter or other unsuitable methods which are likely to cause damage to arrises or increase the width of joints.

Widening of the joint and the use of over-rich pointing will change the appearance of a brick building.

Loose pointing should be carefully raked out manually, using a knife or spike to a depth of at least 25mm or twice the width of the joint. For the repointing of finely jointed work (which is rarely necessary), a hacksaw blade held manually is a suitable tool for cleaning out the joint. Cutting out, using a sharp chisel and a small catchie hammer, may be necessary where there is a hard, cement-rich mortar - usually dating from a previous repointing operation. Due to its impermeability this will cause stones or bricks to erode more rapidly than the joint itself. The removal of hard mortar should be carried out with great care however, and should not be attempted if it will cause more damage to the fabric than if the hard mortar is left until it was loosened sufficiently to allow easier removal.

When repointing, a sound example of original pointing should, where possible, be found in a sheltered part of the building and carefully matched in mix and finish in the new work. In choosing an example to copy, however, care should be taken to ensure that it is not in fact inappropriate later work which is mistakenly selected.

In cases where it is impossible to copy an original mortar or the facilities for analysis are unavailable, a mix should be chosen which is compatible with the porosity and strength of the particular stones or bricks in a wall and suitable for the degree of exposure to the weather of a particular location. The general principle is that the mortar should be slightly weaker than the stone or brick. Mortar which is harder will prevent moisture from evaporating out through the joints so that instead it comes out only through the stones or bricks, thereby increasing the rate of decay and leaving the hard mortar standing proud. For this reason the inclusion

of any cement in a mix should, wherever possible, be avoided. Non-hydraulic lime mortar should normally be made up in the form of coarse stuff from lime putty and aggregate and allowed to mature before use. The type of aggregate should be matched as far as possible to that in the original mortar, but it is also important to ensure that it is well graded with appropriate proportions of fine to coarse sharp grains, and that it is well washed. As a general guide a proportion of 1 lime to 2 or 3 aggregate is likely to be appropriate. The use of pozzolanic additives to improve long-term durability of non-hydraulic mortar may also be considered where appropriate. In difficult conditions it may be necessary to provide some degree of hydraulic set to the mortar, either by the use of a natural moderately hydraulic lime or by the addition of pozzolanic agents to a non-hydraulic mix.

Other additives and pigments should always be avoided and the correct colour should be obtained by adjusting the aggregates, although care should be taken not to use too much stone or brick dust as this can cause cracking of the mortar.

The mortar should be packed firmly into the joint using a pointing key after all loose material has been flushed out and the joint wetted to avoid suction.

The joint should be finished in accordance with the original type where there is evidence of it. This is particularly applicable where joints are finished with a special treatment (provided this is original and not recent), galleting, or cherry-cocking etc., or for ashlar masonry with extremely narrow joints, filled with screened lime putty. The repointing of the latter is rarely needed, but if it is, it requires the skilled use of specialist techniques.

Rubble work which was historically "slaister", or harl pointed, should only have this treatment reproduced in soft lime mortar.

For joints which are not specially treated, a flush finish, fractionally recessed, is usually appropriate. On no account should mortar be spread beyond the joint on to the face of stones or bricks.

Where arrises are decayed, the mortar should be set back to be within the joint width proper, so as to avoid feather edges, which will soon crack away allowing water penetration. In masonry which is not finely finished, eg. wide-jointed brickwork, rubble stonework etc., it is appropriate to finish the joint by brushing the mortar with a bristle brush just after the initial set. Joints should not be smoothed off with a steel trowel.

Relatively recent forms of joint finish, such as "strap" or "ribbon" pointing raised above the surface, "bucket-handle", "weather-struck" etc., usually carried out in hard, cement-rich mortars, are normally inappropriate in historic building work. Such methods of repointing are among the most frequent causes of damage to the character of old buildings and also of damage to the masonry of which they are built.

A sample of pointing should always be approved by the architect before work proceeds.

4.10 REPAIR OF CHIMNEYSTALKS

As exposed features of a building, chimneystalks are particularly vulnerable to decay, both from erosion of stonework or brickwork by the action of rain, wind, or frost and by chemical attack caused by sulphates in the flue gases. When sulphates get into the joints, expansion of the mortar can create a wedging effect causing general instability and often a leaning over of the stalk, aided by the wetting and drying of the side of the stalk exposed

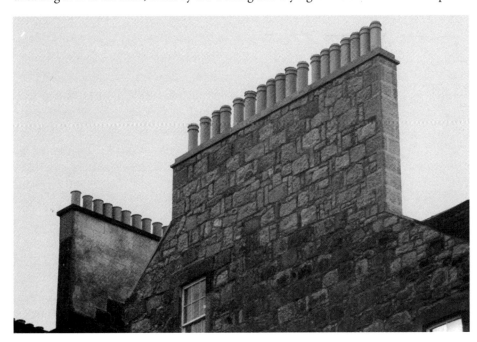

Compared to the cement rendered stalk behind, this rubble and dressed stone chimney has been well reconstructed and furnished with the appropriate cans.

Careful repointing of ashlar chimney stalks using a soft lime mortar.

Coade Stone has been used for the decorative elements on this late 18th Century building. Although it possesses exceptional weathering characteristics, details such as finials can fail due to rust expansion of metal armatures. Great care will be necessary to achieve a suitable mix for repairs.

to the prevailing wind and rain. Internal inspection is strongly advised in such cases.

Where decay is confined to individual stones or bricks these may be cut out and replaced to match, or where the erosion of mortar is not in full depth, repointing will suffice, but if a combination of the factors described above applies it will be necessary to dismantle a stalk and rebuild it. In this case a measured survey should be carried out and the sound units numbered in order to facilitate an accurate reconstruction.

In the case of early stalks, and where there is not a serious lean, it is preferable to consider stabilisation in situ to avoid the risk of an unacceptable degree of damage to original fabric which dismantling may cause. Where the existing flue is wide and straight enough, this may be done by inserting a pipe of stainless steel, with a gap of at least 100mm between it and the inner face of the original flue, so that this may act as both a flue liner and as permanent shuttering to a reinforced concrete lining to the stalk. The use of a lightweight concrete lining system may also be considered.

It is always important to ensure that a flue remains open in order to maintain ventilation, preferably at both top and bottom.

Where a chimneystalk which is important to the design of a building has earlier been reduced in height it should be reinstated in its original form provided evidence for this exists. Proposals for removing a chimneystalk will not normally be acceptable, except where it is agreed to be an intrusive later addition and is in poor condition. Listed building consent would be required.

Badly damaged or missing chimney cans should be reinstated to the original pattern. If fractured, valuable ceramic pots or fine decorative ones can be repaired by "stitching" across the fracture. This work should be carried out be a specialist.

4.11 REPAIR OF TERRACOTTA AND FAIENCE

Such work should only be carried out by specialist conservators. Techniques may include the consolidation of an eroding underbody exposed by the loss of the fireskin, possibly using an alkoxysilane, although this should be approached with caution; the

careful filling of small voids with special mortars; the withdrawal of rusting iron fixings and replacement with non-ferrous material; the protection of vulnerable projecting features with lead flashings unobtrusively placed etc.

Coade Stone, a patent form of terracotta, appeared in the late eighteenth century and was used in refined decorative work, often with the intention of simulating stone. The most widespread use of terracotta was, however, from about the end of the first quarter of the nineteenth century until the second decade of the twentieth, although thin faience cladding continued to be popular for buildings such as cinemas, hotels, shops etc. in the 1920s and 30s.

Terracotta usually performs well if water can be prevented from penetrating. This can occur if, due to defective firing, there are faults in glazing or in the hard fireskin, which, once breached, can lead to the rapid deterioration of the weaker underbody due to frost action or the crystallisation of soluble salts. Glazing of the fireskin can also be damaged by aggressive cleaning using acid.

Scotland possesses relatively few terracotta and faience buildings. Those that survive, as above should be repaired using authentic replacement blocks and not refaced totally in GRC as the example below.

In addition, water may enter via cracks caused by stress, resulting from differential movement between the terracotta blocks and the back-up structure. Water penetration may also be via hairline cracks in the mortar between blocks which was often originally of too hard a mix to allow for flexibility of movement or to allow moisture to evaporate once it had entered.

One of the most serious results of water penetration is the rusting of iron or steel members used to fix the terracotta to the underlying structure. Unless there are tell-tale stains or spalling of the arrises, such damage may not be apparent from the ground and may only come to light when its effects are far advanced, causing major cracking and loosening of units. Non-destructive techniques of investigation could be of considerable use in identifying such problems once they are more fully developed.

Rusted fixings which are causing structural failure should be dealt with by carefully removing the terracotta units and, where possible, completely de-rusting and treating the fixings. Where corrosion is very severe, however, it will be necessary to replace the fixings in stainless steel or non-ferrous metal. Broken units of terracotta may be repaired by dowelling and bonding with epoxy resin.

Where replacement blocks are needed these should be obtainable from one of a small number of manufacturers still in operation. They should match the existing ones in quality, size, colour, and finish. GRC or GRP should not be used as an alternative.

Where it appears that corroded fixings are not a problem, in situ repairs may be carried out by grouting voids behind blocks with low viscosity resin and by refixing loose blocks by drilling and anchoring them with small-diameter stainless steel ties.

The repointing of defective joints should be carried out with a mortar mix which is weaker than the units themselves, to allow for the evaporation of moisture through the joint, but particular care should be taken to ensure that the joints are solidly filled.

Small-scale repairs to individual blocks may, however, be carried out with a special mortar to match the terracotta, using techniques similar to those for plastic repairs to stonework (where approved) and taking care to avoid feather-edging. Colour matching of such special mortars should be achieved by choice of aggregate, not the use of pigments which usually leach out in time, causing the repair to appear unsightly.

Large-scale plastic repairs are not appropriate, nor is the facing-up of damaged terracotta with mortar followed by overall painting as this will completely change the character of the building.

4.12 REPAIR OF EXTERNAL RENDER AND HARLING

There are many types of external render or harling, characteristic of different periods and regions and applied for different reasons to various kinds of backing material.

Harling removed from a rubble wall to make it look historic, but leading to damp penetration.

Each type, and its particular finish and associated details, is usually an essential part of the original character of the building to which it is applied, or part of a significant later remodelling which gives the building its present character. It is important that this character is not damaged by inappropriate methods of repair and materials, and analysis of the existing render should be a prerequisite of repair.

Renders or harling should not be removed in order to expose, for example, rubble stonework, which was not intended to be exposed, nor should it be removed where there are good reasons for render having been applied at a later date. In many instances the replacement of now missing harling or render is appropriate, although this would require listed building consent. It

A situation where harling, or roughcast as this appears to be, should not have been used. The ashlar has exfoliated, probably due to being built on the cant, and the masonry has been irreversibly rendered and painted

should always be to a traditional recipe appropriate to the structure concerned. Prior to rendering, the building should always be photographed for documentary evidence of earlier openings etc. which may be covered up.

There may also be cases, however, where the later application of render detracts from the proper character of a building and damages the original design intention. If so, and subject to accurate evidence of the original appearance, the removal of the render (for which listed building consent is required) may be considered acceptable. Other factors also need to be taken into account, nevertheless, such as the risk of damp penetration if the render is removed. It may also be found to be necessary to carry out repairs to the original underlying material following the removal of the render which, if considerable, may make the proposal impractical and costly.

4.12.1 MEDIUM TO LOW-STRENGTH LIME-BASED COVERINGS

These are either flat-finished renders or textured (the latter variously known as harling, rough-cast, or wet-dash). They are intended to act as a protective outer layer to a building. Periodically they require extensive repair or replacement, the frequency of which largely depends on degree of exposure.

To function correctly, the harling or render must be no stronger than the material to which it is applied in order to be sufficiently flexible to accommodate movement and to allow moisture to evaporate freely from it. Hard, cement-rich mixes should not be used to replace such lime-based coverings as their lack of flexibility will cause them to crack, allowing water to penetrate and be trapped, eventually leading to the failure of the covering and the decay of the masonry itself.

Wherever possible an existing render or harling should be analysed so that the mix may be copied, and a sheltered area should be examined in order to determine the original colour and texture of the finish. The latter should be achieved by the choice of aggregates. Pigments should be avoided, except where the use of natural earth pigments is appropriate. It is, however, impossible to generalise, and mixes will vary from area to area and according to building type and period. Bonding agents should be avoided except where granites and whin stones are involved. The wall should be wetted before the application of the harling or render in order to reduce suction.

Where the wall has an undulating surface, eg. a rubble stone wall, this should be accepted and no attempt made to dub out the surface for the sake of providing a flat finish.

The original details at openings, corners etc., should be followed.

The harling or render may be left uncoated or finished with limewash, if appropriate, but on no account should an impermeable paint system be used as this will lead to the entrapment of moisture.

4.12.2 SMOOTH RENDERS OR STUCCOS

These were most often applied to brickwork although occasionally to rubble stone, often with the object of simulating expensive ashlar but are comparatively rare in Scotland. They were capable of incorporating the full range of architectural features usually associated with masonry. Wall surfaces are often channelled to give an appearance of rustication, or lined-out in imitation of finely jointed work.

From the mid eighteenth-century oil mastic stuccos were produced and in 1794 Parker's Roman Cement was patented, a quick-setting natural hydraulic cement which was widely used throughout the nineteenth century. It is characteristically a buff colour, and was often finished by a wash of lime and copperas.

In the mid nineteenth-century artificial cements were developed by firing together a combination of ground limestone and clay called Portland Cement. When mixed with sand, or lime and sand, these cements produced smooth renders or stuccos of high strength and impermeability.

Major failure of dense impervious render on an early reinforced concrete building (1904) not helped by lack of key.

Failure of these high-strength stuccos is usually caused by water penetration through cracks, or by defects resulting from lack of maintenance, leading to loss of adhesion. Surface deterioration may be caused by the crystallisation of soluble salts.

4.13   REPAIR OF EARTH WALLS

The use of unbaked earth for the walls of vernacular buildings was an early form of construction in this country. Its use was widespread in areas where the soil contained clay, silt, or sand, until around the mid nineteenth-century when bricks and stonework became readily available. Methods of construction and the names given to them vary according to the areas in which they were traditionally used, and in these areas surviving examples may be seen, although sometimes now obscured by a later covering.

Generally, however, earth buildings are relatively rare and their loss in some areas (eg. the Carse of Gowrie, the Mearns and the Laigh of Moray) is of particular concern. It is important, therefore, that the buildings which do remain are retained and that when repairs are needed, they are carried out in an appropriate manner with the correct materials.

Water penetration is usually the chief cause of decay, so they were traditionally protected at the head by an overhanging eaves and at the base by a stone or brick plinth to prevent rising damp or damage by rain splash. Surface protection is often provided by limewashed earth or lime renders. The proper maintenance of these elements is essential if rapid deterioration is to be avoided. It is essential that the structure is able to breath: impervious paint finishes or hard impervious surface render or harling should never be used.

Excavation by masonry bees can occasionally be a problem for earth walls.

Pisé is the most common form of earth walling still to be found in occupied dwelling houses. Here the clay is tempered with sharp sand and gravel. The main pisé areas are centred on the Laigh of Moray, Buchan, the Howe of the Mearns, Carse of Gowrie, Coldingham Moor and Dumfriesshire. An older form known as "mudwall" used chopped vegetable matter to temper the clay and is similar to English cob. Stone faced earth walls are commonplace in the Western Isles and in the form known as "claywall" in east central Scotland. This is often mistaken for small scale rubble walling. Other types of clay wall with stones in the facework include "clay and bool" or Auchinhalrig work named after the village in the Laigh of Moray where it originated.

Some earlier types of mudwall have a timber core, the most common types being "kebber and mott" and "stake and rice". Kebber and mott is a form of palisade construction using spruce poles to form a base for the mott or mud. Stake and rice, the Scots term for wattle, can have mud applied as in wattle and daub. Variations include the use of horizontal spars to support the daub, straw matt, and straw or heather rope to replace the "rice" or wattle.

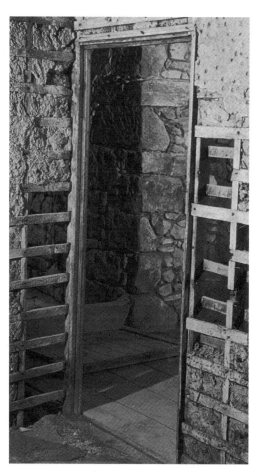

The discovery of old timber and daubed partitions (here 17th Century, though the door is later) should result in accurate recording and then repair using the most sympathetic materials.

The other type of earth wall found in Scotland is turf construction. This can take a number of forms but the two most commonly found are: greenturf, laid grass to grass and earth to earth alternatively; fale, a parallelogram-shaped block laid herring bone fashion, often cut from peat. Divet is sometimes laid between the individual courses of fale to form "fale and divet," divet being a very thin horizontal layer.

A hybrid construction comprising alternating layers of stone and turf is also found, usually in farm steadings but occasionally in the internal and external gables of dwellings.

In every case it is important to record as accurately as possible the constructional technique as found and to replicate this as closely as possible in any reconstruction or reinstatement work.

Repairs

Each of the above regional types and some others not mentioned, have their own particular characteristics which should be carefully respected and followed when making repairs. Unfortunately, unsympathetic methods of repair are common, eg. patching decayed areas with cement-rich mortars or filling holes with concrete blocks or bricks. These incompatible materials can cause damage to adjacent parts of the original structure and must be avoided.

A particular problem associated with the repair of earth walls is the need to achieve sufficient compaction and to minimise drying out and shrinkage so that the repair is compatible with the original work. Surface repairs and their key with the old material may be achieved by cutting back the area to be repaired so that it is undercut at the edges, and the existing surfaces are then wetted with a mist spray to achieve integration with the newly applied material which should be mixed to the consistency of a stiff porridge.

It is important that any material used in these repairs is as close a match as possible with the original, to ensure compatibility and integration with the old base. An analysis of the old material should be made in order to achieve as close a mix as possible.

Compression of the new material behind a shutter board can provide good compaction, but it must be appreciated that although a surface repair may maintain integrity with the old material, it is unlikely to achieve the original strength.

Tapered oak pegs may be driven into the old wall in order to help the key, provided the surface will accept them. Alternatively tile slips set into slots may be considered, although as tiles are an alien material they should be used with caution.

Deep deterioration of the wall will require removal of the whole thickness and its replacement using shuttering on both sides.

Where open fissures have occurred in the wall as a result of water penetration they will need to be filled and can be stitched in a variety of ways, depending on the stability of the wall. The fissure will need to be cut out as for surface repairs. The source of water penetration should of course be removed. If masonry bees are responsible, the advice of Scottish Natural Heritage should be sought before blocking holes, since some species are protected.

A degree of dampness within an earth structure is usually an essential characteristic of the material. Damp-proof courses should usually be avoided, therefore, as they are likely to lead to an undesirable degree of drying out of the wall, reducing the bond of its materials and causing powdering of the surface. If, as a result of serious rising damp, the introduction of a damp-proof course becomes necessary, it should be applied only within the stone base and never within the earth structure itself. Excessive dampness within the building is likely to be caused by factors that can be solved in other ways, for instance the reduction of the external ground level, provision of drainage etc.

4.14   REPAIR OF CONCRETE STRUCTURES

In Scotland, mass concrete was probably in use as early as 1828 and concrete was being produced and widely used in buildings in the Carse of Gowrie from about the middle of the nineteenth century. In the late nineteenth century, concrete was sometimes used as an unreinforced filling material between iron or rolled steel joists in floors and flat roofs, usually with clinker as a main ingredient of the aggregate.

If water is allowed to penetrate such material, eg. through a defective roof finish, the clinker will expand and, because allowance was not usually made for movement, the resulting pressure can cause bulging and cracking in perimeter parapets, walls etc. If diagnosed at an early stage, the problem may not be serious and the prevention of further water penetration by the repair of the roof finish, together with the pointing of any cracks which may have occurred in the masonry, may suffice. If allowed to continue unchecked, however, extensive structural repairs may be needed, possibly including the removal of the concrete in order to treat or replace rusted beams and the tying-in or partial rebuilding of distorted masonry.

In the early use of reinforced concrete it was not uncommon for inadequate cover to be given to the reinforcement, resulting in its corrosion and expansion and spalling of the concrete. Water may also enter because of the concrete becoming porous through leaching of soluable materials. Chemical degradation of the concrete may also occur from impurities contained in the sand or aggregate, or from additives introduced to increase workability.

Superficial methods of repair should be avoided, eg. the surface spraying on of new concrete without dealing with underlying problems, such as rusted reinforcement. Such a method is also likely to be unacceptable because of the effect it may have on the appearance of the structure in altering the profile of members.

Where extreme degradation of elements of the structure has taken place, it may be necessary to dismantle and rebuild. New reinforcement should be given adequate cover and be well galvanised or epoxy coated. Alternatively stainless steel may be used.

The majority of repairs, however, will involve the removal of cracked and spalled concrete in order to expose the reinforcement so that it may be completely de-rusted by chemical or mechanical means, followed by anti-corrosion treatment. Where the cover is adequate a new plain concrete mix may then be applied. Where the cover is not sufficient, however, a mix containing a polymer may be used, or possibly an epoxy resin mortar if strength is an important consideration. Permeability may also be reduced by sealing both the repaired and unrepaired areas.

Work to reinforced concrete should not usually be undertaken without the advice of a structural engineer.

Two examples of spalling concrete caused by the rusting and expansion of reinforcement, the lower example aggravated by frost action. The reinforcement should be exposed, de-rusted, and treated, and the concrete made good, possibly incorporating a cementitous polymer in the mix if the cover is inadequate. In the top example the ingress of the water must clearly be stopped.

4.15   REPAIR OF IRONWORK

4.15.1 THE NATURE OF WROUGHT IRON

Wrought iron is produced by means of working pig iron (smelted iron ore) to remove virtually all carbon and other impurities, followed by further reheating and reworking to improve tensile strength.

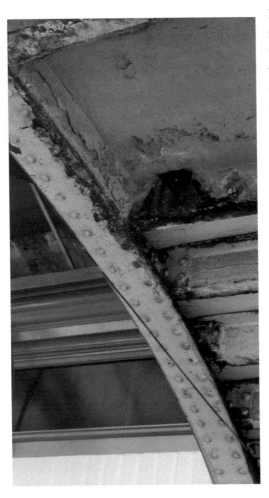

Corrosion of the wrought iron members of a staircase by water penetration threatens its stability and safety.

From the fourteenth century, when the blast furnace was developed, until the eighteenth century, the use of wrought iron in buildings was largely confined to the ironmongery of doors, window ferramenta, straps, tie bars, and for gates and railings. By the end of the eighteenth century, technological improvements allowed for the manufacture of rolled sections which could be used structurally. Scotland has a number of bridges dating from the 1820s which employ wrought iron. From the 1840s rolling machinery was introduced which speeded up production.

With the introduction of methods for producing mild steel in large quantities, first invented in 1856 and widely used by the 1880s, the labour-intensiveness and relatively high cost of wrought iron production were much reduced. Today, however, apart from recycled material, new wrought iron is only available in small quantities.

Wrought iron has good tensile strength, and when used structurally this quality is usually exploited, eg. it was used for arched members of roofs and arcades, astragals or glazing bars particularly in curved roofs, and tie rods etc. Wrought iron can be identified, where a fracture has occurred, by the fibrous nature of its internal structure, formed by beating or rolling. Characteristic structural details are jointing by forge welding, joints resembling timber methods, and the riveting of sections together to form composite members.

4.15.2   THE NATURE OF CAST IRON

Cast iron is made by pouring molten pig iron into moulds. Although regarded as poor in tension it is strong in compression. Structurally, it is most suitable for columns, and when used for beams the bottom flanges need to be considerably thicker than for wrought iron beams. Its uses for semi-structural and decorative members are almost unlimited, eg. brackets, staircases, railings and balustrades, roof ridges, brattishing and finials, gutters and downpipes etc. Cast iron can be identified, where fractures have occurred, by its relatively homogeneous, crystalline structure and by characteristic casting defects such as blow holes. Further means of identification are slightly raised lines on the surface created by joints in moulds. A number of Scottish bridges dating from the early nineteenth century use cast iron, or a mixture of cast and wrought iron elements.

4.15.3 CORROSION

Both wrought and cast iron possess generally good anti-corrosion properties, but where they are likely to be exposed to water and air it is essential that they are properly protected by a system of coatings of paint and that this is carefully maintained annually, especially in a marine environment. If unattended to, even small defects in coatings can allow water to enter, causing corrosion to develop underneath the coating, which will eventually blister off to reveal areas of rust.

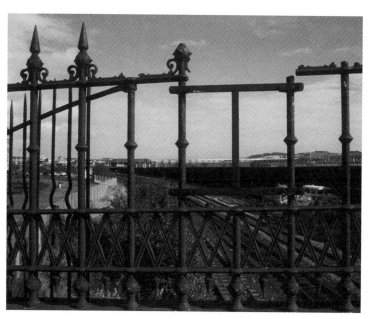

Strap Repairs to ornamental cast iron railings which, even if structurally adequate, are totally unacceptable in terms of appearance.

On no account should rust be overpainted. Defective areas should be dealt with by removing layers of paint and rust completely before priming and repainting. This may be done by methods such as simple scrapers, wire brushes, and sand papers, or by the use of roto-strippers or abrasive flap wheels, although these will not deal with detailed areas and should be used with care to avoid damage to the surrounding fabric.

Where corrosion is extensive, often hidden under many layers of defective old paint which is also likely to clog up and obscure the detail of the ironwork, it is best that it is comprehensively removed. Before this is done the paint layers should be analysed to enable an original colour scheme to be reinstated in appropriate cases.

Sandblasting is an effective method of cleaning for cast iron. If a building is in an area frequented by the public, however, the amount of gritty dust created by dry sandblasting is likely to be unacceptable, particularly if the paint is lead-based and therefore a health hazard. Wet-blasting, ie. grit applied with a high-pressure water spray, or the use of a needle gun are preferable for in situ cleaning, although the latter should be used with care to avoid damage to the surface of the ironwork or of enrichment which may be of a different, softer material. Tannic acid based rust converters can be used to neutralise rust or to treat delicate areas. Cleaning should be carried out as short a time as possible before the application of the first stage of the treatment process, in order to prevent the development of rust.

The abrasive methods described above are not, however, to be recommended for the softer wrought iron. Flame cleaning, followed by the use of a wire brush, is the most suitable method, even though slower (fire precautions are necessary if work is executed in situ).

Where a structure can be dismantled, or where some dismantling is in any case necessary in order to remedy structural faults, cleaning may be carried out under more controlled conditions, possibly in a workshop. This will also allow for all-round treatment, particularly of joints. Before any dismantling is carried out, a structure should be recorded by means of drawings and photographs and each element numbered with a tag and on the drawing.

4.15.4 STRUCTURAL REPAIR

The removal of paint and rust may reveal further structural defects, both in the overall structure and in individual members, which were not apparent in an initial survey of their condition.

Movement may have taken place, possibly causing a redistribution of loads and the introduction of stresses in areas not originally designed to take them. Engineering advice should be obtained to determine whether such stresses can be accepted without structural risk, or whether action is needed. This may take the form of partial dismantling and re-erection, or the introduction of measures such as tie rods or additional elements for strengthening purposes such as plates (eg. on the bottom flanges of beams), or even additional beams or columns. The latter may have the effect of radically changing the appearance of a structure, and should only be considered as a last resort and subject to statutory consents.

Movement of the structure, either by load pattern behaviour or thermally, may cause members to fracture, particularly in the case of cast iron which is subject to tensile stress. Cast-iron columns may also fracture if they become filled with water which then freezes, either due to leaks or because they are intentionally designed to function as rainwater pipes, which may then have become blocked. In the latter case it may be possible to introduce a lining during repairs; alternatively, consideration may be given to the provision of separate rhonepipes, if this can be achieved unobtrusively. Fractures in cast iron may be repaired in situ by "cold" metal stitching, which is both effective and less obtrusive.

Repair by welding is often very difficult to achieve successfully with cast iron, and then only usually for relatively small sections in workshop conditions. Welding is, however, an effective means of repairing broken sections of wrought iron or fixing on new pieces in place of corroded parts.

Where relatively small members are built into a masonry wall (eg. window bars etc.) and the end is badly corroded, it is sensible to fix a new tip in brass, bronze or stainless steel, rather than in iron which may rust again in due course.

A structural repair may sometimes be achieved by reinstating a lost member, which should be copied from adjacent existing members. In the case of cast iron, patterns may be taken for a new casting to be made in an iron foundry, or, if dismantling of the structure has been necessary, an original section may be used as a pattern.

New castings should also be made of elements which are badly corroded beyond structural effectiveness, and also of corroded or missing non-structural members which are important in the overall design.

Where it is necessary to replace wrought-iron members, recycled wrought iron should be used or new wrought iron obtained, if available.

4.15.5 PROTECTIVE COATINGS

When de-rusting and the necessary repair or replacement of elements have been completed, ironwork should be fully and carefully protected by an appropriate system of coatings. Before coatings are applied, any water-holding pockets as well as any structurally non-significant but nevertheless defacing areas of corrosion, may be made good by the use of metal fillers.

Immediately prior to treatment, the ironwork should be inspected for signs of rust which may have developed since the completion of de-rusting, particularly in conditions conducive to condensation. If any rust exists it should be removed by a flash flame clean, subject to necessary fire precautions being taken. On no account should coatings be applied in damp conditions.

The choice of a system of coatings will depend on such considerations as local environmental conditions, policy on maintenance, ease or difficulty of access, and the degree of historical interest of the structure or of any early paint which may remain. As an example, however, a system may comprise two priming coats of red lead or non-toxic zinc phosphate, then two coats of micaceous iron oxide, followed by two finishing coats of exterior quality oil paint.

4.16 REPAIR OF EXTERNAL AND INTERNAL JOINERY

Joinery forming an integral part of a building may include such external features as cupolas, balustrades of roof platforms and balconies, ornamental bargeboards, eaves cornices, windows and window surrounds, doors and doorcases, porches etc., and such internal features as wall panelling, shutters, dados, skirtings, overmantels, doors, together with architraves and overdoors, panelled ceilings, floorboarding, staircases and stair balustrades etc. These will very often be essential elements in the original design of a building or of a significant later phase of alteration, and as such make a major contribution to a building's interest and importance. Details of joinery such as mouldings, carved decoration etc., are often valuable aids in indicating the date of a building or in identifying a craftsman or designer.

It is essential, therefore, in view of the relative vulnerability of joinery, particularly when external, to retain and preserve original material wherever possible by regular inspection and careful maintenance, and to carry out repairs when necessary using appropriate methods and materials.

Sensitive repairs to an early 18th century timber staircase. Missing balusters have been reinstated to match existing, but worn treads have not been levelled.

Many of the considerations which apply to the repair of carpentry (see 4.6 Repair of structural timbers) apply also to the repair of joinery. Damp penetration and fungus and insect attack are again the main agents of decay and their causes should be dealt with before repairs are carried out.

External joinery should be protected by regular painting. Lead weatherings on timber cornices, pediments of doorcases etc., should be properly maintained where they exist, or introduced where appropriate, provided this can be done without adversely affecting the appearance of the feature or of the building as a whole.

Voids formed within the carcassing of joinery, both external and internal, should be adequately ventilated to allow any moisture which may enter to evaporate readily before fungal growth can occur, and also to guard against conditions conducive to insect attack.

Joinery items much in use can be subject to considerable strain, leading to the loosening of joints and eventual fracture of sections or general collapse. To guard against this, such fittings as hinges on doors and casement windows, and cords and pulleys on sash windows, should be kept in good order and replaced to match if broken beyond repair.

The fundamental principle to adopt in repairing historic joinery is to replace only what is necessary, using timber of matching species and type of grain. Where new pieces are required they should be carefully jointed in, using the same technology as was used for the original in order to maintain the degree of flexibility necessary in features which are built up of many sections.

Where original detailing survives, piecing-in of new mouldings must exactly match the existing so that profiles and mitres run

Although with carpentry it is possible to use unseasoned timber, joinery requires all timber to be fully seasoned. An important principle is that the moisture content of timber used in joinery repairs should match the old. This is necessary in order to avoid differential movement between old and new, and consequential distortion, particularly in external work and is also necessary where any adhesive has been used. In the worst cases, a new piece of unseasoned timber may eventually fall out, especially with repairs using very small slips of timber. These should in any case be used with caution as shrinkage cracks may form around them, allowing water to enter and cause decay.

It is often possible to dismantle part of a piece of joinery to facilitate the carrying out of a proper repair. It is rarely necessary, therefore, to resort to alternative methods of repair which should only be considered when working in situ is unavoidable. All joinery repairs should in any case be carried out by expert craftsmen, and this is an essential requirement where any dismantling is involved. Before any dismantling is carried out the positions of all existing members should be carefully recorded. Careless dismantling can cause considerable damage, particularly when timbers are decayed. This can often be the case when dismantling is carried out by other tradesmen in the course of their own work, eg. the removal of skirtings or floorboards for the installation of heating pipes or electrical wiring. In such cases, damaged floorboards are frequently crudely replaced using softwood in place of elm or oak, and two narrow boards in place of an original wide one. When service installations affect historic joinery, an experienced joiner should be responsible for the careful lifting of boarding or removal of sections of skirting etc., and for carrying out any necessary repairs before reinstatement by splicing new pieces in matching timber. Splits should be repaired by glueing and clamping, with fixing blocks screwed on to the rear. When access to service runs is likely to be required regularly, floorboards should be discreetly fixed with screws in order to facilitate access and prevent damage.

It is particularly important when repairing moulded and carved joinery to ensure that the maximum amount of original material is retained. Where replacement is unavoidable, the new work should follow the existing work precisely, and where appropriate, detailed drawings should be prepared and patterns made in advance. The work should be finished by hand: machine-run finishes should always be avoided.

The use of substitute materials such as GRP to simulate moulded or carved joinery is inappropriate.

Where a carved or moulded section of joinery survives intact only on its outer face, the bulk of the member behind it having decayed, it is important, if at all possible, that the authentic carving be retained in situ. In order to achieve this it

The replacement of the original panelled door with a modern factory made hardwood version has completely ruined the original design of a unified doorway

may be necessary, following the removal of the decay, to refix the old work by means of adhesive to a new backing piece. Alternatively it may be possible, if the extent of decay is not general, to grout the voids with low viscosity epoxy resin but consideration of this method should be approached with caution and not used for external locations where moisture may become trapped behind the resin and thus accelerate decay.

Where valuable surfaces themselves are weakened by decay or insect attack, consideration may be given to strengthening them by impregnation with a consolidant such as an epoxy resin or an acrylic resin, which have different properties appropriate to particular conditions. Impregnation is achieved by a slow process of injection and must be entrusted to a specialist conservator.

When repairs are carried out to windows, only those sections which have decayed sufficiently seriously should be replaced: wholesale renewal for the sake of convenience should always be avoided. The profiles of decayed sections of astragals etc., which need splicing should be copied exactly and be precisely married into the existing work. In the process of carrying out such work, all old glass should be carefully retained for reuse and not replaced with modern sheet glass.

When the complete replacement of a badly decayed window is necessary, the existing design should normally be reproduced exactly. On no account should an inappropriate modern replacement be substituted, even if superficially similar, eg. a design intended to appear like a double-hung sash but in fact using top-hung lights. Substitute materials such as UPVC are inappropriate in an historic context.

Repairs may offer the opportunity for removing inappropriate or damaging later alterations and for reinstating an original design, provided that detailed evidence exists for this and subject to the necessary statutory contents. Caution should be exercised in considering such proposals, however, as alterations may contribute to the cumulative historic interest of a building, eg. the insertion of nineteenth-century plate glass sashes in place of small-paned sashes in a Georgian facade may be part of a significant phase of alteration to the building as a whole, or may possibly relate to a contemporary redesigning of the interiors.

4.17 REPAIR OF GLASS

The repair of historically important glazing is the work of a specialist conservator. There is now virtually no medieval stained or plain glazing in Scotland but there are many fine examples of later and particularly Victorian work.

The problem of bulging or sagging stained or plain glass windows is most commonly found in churches but can also occur in municipal buildings and large Victorian mansions. It is usually caused by expansion of the leadwork causing movement, and is often due to insufficient saddle bars or tie bars (ferramenta) supporting the windows at regular centres, thus allowing the weight of the glass to pull on the lead cames as the cames have become brittle. South-facing windows are particularly affected by daily temperature changes causing movement in the cames but the temperature differential between the outside and inside of the building can have a similar effect. Daylight gaps around the edge of the individual quarries can allow rainwater to penetrate and are often found to be crudely pointed up with cement mortar in an attempt to keep water out, thus exacerbating the situation by adding to the weight of the cames. Horizontal cames which have lost their putty can also hold water which can freeze and expand. An analysis of cracking in the glass may determine what remedial strengthening in the way of additional saddle bars is required.

The first effort should be to determine if the window can be repaired in situ by the addition of further saddle bars (always to be in non-ferrous metal) and if the cames can be gently eased back to the vertical. Saddle bars may be better on the inside of the window in any case. The addition of secondary glazing (see below) may add the necessary weatherproofing to retain the window in place. Specialist advice should be sought as many sagging windows are constructed from the unusually thick "Norman Slab" or "Early English" type of glass which has a greater expansion differential with surrounding glass and leadwork and secondary glazing with the associated "greenhouse" effect can often exacerbate the problem. If the lead cames have clearly perished and the glass pieces cracked by the movement then it will prove more economic to take the window out and re-lead it. This is not nearly such a major undertaking as it may seem but it is the work of a stained glass specialist. All lead cames eventually deteriorate due to continual movement, so all windows require re-leading at some stage.

The window must first be recorded in situ by photography and/or drawings and adequate scaffolding provided to allow this. Historic glass is at particular risk from scaffolding of course, and scaffolders must be made aware of its importance and the need to provide additional restraint at windows to reduce putlogs in the vicinity of the glass. An unrestricted working area is necessary for the glazier. Research should also be undertaken into the history of the glass and cames as knowledge of former restorations can be particularly informative. Sometimes names and dates can be found scratched on the cames or the glass itself. A stonemason should be on hand to assist the glazier in freeing the lead frame from the masonry by removing the saddle bars and easing the lead from the stone. If this has been heavily pointed then every effort must be made to avoid damage to the glass and surrounding leadwork. Sometimes the stained glass is contained within a timber sub-frame which allows easier removal. Great care must be taken in transporting the window to the workshop (and vice versa) as this may cause additional breakages if it is not fully protected.

The specialist will repair the window on the bench using a full size rubbing of the leadwork, and will simply replace like with like. Points to watch are:-

● firstly, that the came pattern is faithfully reproduced and no "short-cuts" are taken. This is particularly important with figure work where the original designer has usually worked out the figure and particularly the head into a distinctive came pattern. The same width of came must be used as before so that the template is correctly followed. Old leadwork, particularly that dating to the seventeenth century, should always be retained if in sound condition. If it is beyond repair, samples should be retained and consideration given to melting down and recasting the lead for reuse in place of new lead.

● secondly, the original glass pieces, where cracked, are carefully glued together with special edge-bonding silica-based adhesive rather than replaced with modern glass, unless fragmented. Where edge bonding is not possible, a copper foiling technique should be undertaken. Spurious cames or lead strip "Dutchmen" should not be used to repair cracked pieces, but should be removed only where they are clearly the result of shoddy previous repairs.

Where the original glass has been badly etc.hed by pollution or weathering crust - usually affecting the skin tones and delicate painted face work - a decision may have to be taken with the specialist glazier or glass historian as to replacement with modern glass appropriately painted and fired though one should go to great lengths to preserve original faces. It is also possible to plate over the face areas with localised clear glass in a double came arrangement. The emphasis should always be to keep as much original glass as possible particularly if the window is by a celebrated artist, and overall secondary glazing in situ may be the preferred conservation option in such cases. The removal of dirt and weathering crust should be viewed primarily as a conservation measure rather than improvement of the transparency of the window. The specialist will carefully select cleaning fluids depending on the permanency of the paint film etc., as all glass cleaning methods currently in use are experimental and controversial. If the paintwork or enamel is loose no form of cleaning should be used ideally, and certainly no detergents, bleaches and acids however diluted as this will accelerate deterioration. Water should be used as the first cleaning agent to remove surface dirt and bird droppings and should be preferably distilled, or de-ionised, rather than mains water. The cleaning action can be assisted by the use of a soft brush or cloth. The work should not be undertaken if there is any risk of freezing. The use of special fibre brushes, ideally glass fibre, is the most effective and controllable method of dry cleaning in situ. No sealant or varnish should be applied to the cleaned glass as more damage than protection has resulted in the past from using such coatings.

Once the re-leaded window has been placed back in the opening with the mason having cleared the glazing check of any detritus and repaired any damaged ashlar and is supported with adequate non-ferrous saddle bars, consideration should be given to its protection.

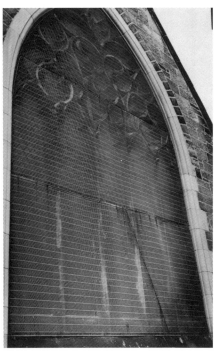

Steel mesh screens have been provided without any regard for the form of the window design and elaborate tracery.

The provision of mesh screens in stainless steel rather than copper or galvanised mild steel is often the very least that can be done particularly if the building is in an urban environment with a risk of vandalism. These will stop hand-thrown missiles but not air gun pellets. The initial appearance may be somewhat alien but the brightness of the screen will soon weather down. Screens should be purpose-made to templates taken from the tracery etc., so that each light has its own screen and the design of the window can be clearly read. The window should not be sheeted across with a single screen. Secondary glazing may be an attractive option if the window reveal is large enough to take it without seriously affecting the appearance of the building. It should be housed in neat non-ferrous frames and must be designed to allow adequate ventilation to the cavity behind, preferably top and bottom or at intermediate levels and should be removable to allow future access for cleaning. A minimum 15mm cavity should be provided for ventilation to avoid condensation. Even more effective however as it removes the risk of condensation forming on the painted surface, is to ventilate the additional glazing internally if the architectural framework will allow this. The whole of the historic glass interior and exterior surfaces are then within a controlled environment. The rather dead appearance that sheets of plain glazing can impart to a building - particularly a church - can be mitigated by the further provision of stainless steel mesh screens - a useful precaution against stone throwing etc., in any case.

Secondary glazing has been installed to protect the stained glass window on the left which, despite loss of lucency giving a rather dead appearance externally, does considerably extend it's life, as long as ventilation is provided.

Polycarbonate sheet should not be used for secondary glazing unless large areas or a weight consideration preclude the use of standard glass but can sometimes be helpful internally at lower levels to prevent the original stained glass being fingered and scratched if it is accessible. Care should be taken not to cause or exacerbate any condensation problem, and allow for any condensate to escape at the base. Access for cleaning the historic glass behind should not be overlooked. It should be remembered that all forms of plastic sheeting are flammable and as such it is not the best protector of valuable glass.

Finally a programme of periodic inspection should be carried out to check the condition of the screens, and any damage to the glass itself by corrosion, condensation or projectile impact. When other building work is going on in the vicinity of historic glass, it will be prudent to protect it, if necessary by temporary removal to safe storage. Ensure that all overhanging branches of trees etc. are lopped to prevent the glass being scratched by wind movement.

In this example, wire guards have been made up to follow the form of the lights they protect. It is possible to design and shape wire guards to carry any architectural form and to have them covered with protective plastic coating to match the colour of the stone surrounding them.

With domestic glazing, the character of the window must be maintained by the use of appropriate glass in repairs. For windows of the Georgian period, crown glass with its inherent curve and sparkle is available from specialist glass manufacturers but may prove too expensive. Good quality cylinder glass is relatively inexpensive however and has some of the characteristics. Avoid using tinted glasses as an attempt at historicism. Original glass should be handled with great care and reused wherever possible. Permanent ventilation to reduce the risk of damaging condensation should be introduced whenever possible. The conservation work on any historic windows should be fully documented and kept in the building's records.

4.18   REPAIR OF PLAIN AND DECORATIVE PLASTERWORK

Non-hydraulic lime is the basis for most traditional plaster used internally, as it is for most traditional external renders.

Gypsum was used for plaster from the mid thirteenth-century but only to a relatively

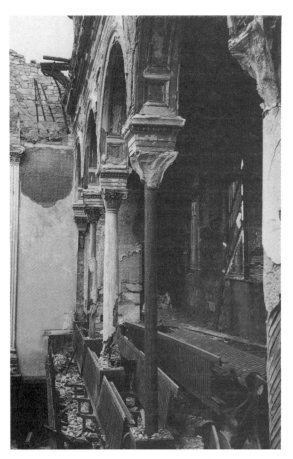

The comparative strength of fibrous plaster is well illustrated in this building which has been roofless for years. Note the spiral lathing to the cast iron columns.

limited extent. By the second half of the eighteenth-century ornament was often cast in gypsum plaster, while from the beginning of the nineteenth century it came to be more generally used for wall and ceiling plasterwork, and various potential varieties were introduced, such as Keene's Cement (1838) and Parian Cement (1846). Metal lathing was introduced in the late nineteenth-century but wooden lathing continued in use for ceilings until the period prior to the Second World War.

Hair is the traditional reinforcing material for the undercoats of both lime and gypsum plasters and may still be obtained for the purpose, but care must be taken that it is of sufficient length and strength. Goat hair is likely to be the most suitable. Hemp may be considered as an alternative to hair.

4.18.1 WALL PLASTER

Although internal wall plasters do not suffer from direct exposure to the elements as do external renders, they may be affected by moisture in walls caused by rising damp, defective pointing, leaking downpipes etc., and all such defects should be remedied before repairs to the plaster are carried out. Where plaster is sufficiently decayed to warrant removal, the wall should be allowed to dry out for as long as possible before the plaster is replaced.

Many of the principles and practices which apply to the repair of external render and harling apply also to internal wall plasters.(see 4.12).

The repair of early wall plaster, especially surviving medieval work, should be approached with particular care. It should not be disturbed unless this is essential, as it may retain painted decoration under later coats of limewash. If the existence of wall paintings is suspected expert advice should be obtained so that careful investigation can be carried out.

Every attempt should be made to retain early wall plaster in situ, eg. by filleting and grouting areas which have become detached from the wall and also, possibly, by providing mechanical fixings with non-ferrous screws. Friable surfaces may be consolidated by limewater treatment.

Efflorescing salts and damp contamination from the wet masonry has led to the breakdown of the plaster, not helped by the emulsion paint not absorbing any condensation.

4.18.2 CEILING PLASTER

Analysis of Defects

When defects are evident, a careful inspection should first be carried out in order to determine the cause or causes prior to formulating proposals for repair.

A ceiling should first be looked at from the floor and a diagrammatic plan made with any obvious defects marked on it. A closer inspection should then be made of the underside from a ladder or platform to determine the seriousness of any cracks (eg their width or whether one side is lower than the other), and of any sagging, and whether the surface of the plaster is weak or crumbly.

The ceiling should then be inspected from above, either from a roof void or by the careful lifting of floorboarding. It will almost certainly be necessary to remove debris and dust with vacuum cleaners and carefully lift out into pails for reinstatement any ash deafening etc., before a detailed inspection can be made of the condition of laths and of the plaster key.

The condition of main beams should be carefully inspected, particularly at the ends where they are built into walls, or under parapet gutters where they may be rotten due to damp penetration. Sagging or cracking in a ceiling may be caused by such defects or possibly by movement in roof trusses or supporting walls: in such cases all necessary structural repairs should be carried out. Repairs to beam ends, fractures along the length of beams, or weak joints should, wherever possible, be carried out in situ in order to avoid disturbing the plasterwork. Plaster ceilings should be supported by careful packing and propping during repairs to beams etc.

Beams immediately above the ceiling should be inspected to see whether they are battened on the underside; if not there may be insufficient key for the plaster if laths are fixed directly to the underside of the beam or if the beam itself is simply hacked.

If there is evidence of damp staining on the plaster and it has a crumbly surface, an inspection should be made of roof coverings or plumbing pipes to determine whether leaks

Restored decorative plasterwork ceilings at Duff House

are occurring and the necessary repairs should then be carried out.

Common defects associated with the plaster itself and its lathing are the rusting of the nails fixing the laths to the ceiling joists, decay of the laths due to insect attack or damp penetration, and defective key because of incorrect spacing of the laths. Sometimes the plaster keys may have broken off, which may be caused by the persistent vibration of a ceiling.

Repairs

Following a careful inspection it will be possible to decide on the necessary extent of repair, for example whether local repairs will suffice or whether, if a ceiling is cracking or sagging seriously over a large area, more comprehensive repairs are necessary.

It is usually possible to repair a ceiling in situ and this should always be the aim. There are however, occasions when some dismantling may be necessary, if, for example, extensive repairs are necessary to supporting beams and joists or if access to the ceiling from above is difficult or impossible. In this case the plasterwork should be carefully cut into sections as defined by mouldings or ribs. Elements such as plaques, pendants etc., should wherever possible, be removed in one piece.

Where sagging is occurring it will usually be necessary to support the ceiling from below. This may be achieved by providing a birdcage scaffolding to carry plywood panels, laid 30mm or so below any projecting moulded ribs or other decorative feature, with the areas between packed up with cushions of foam rubber or felt rolls.

Mixes of plaster for repair work should wherever possible be based on an analysis of the existing work. It is important not to use a hard mix for repairs to a relatively soft existing plaster, as cracking and possibly detachment may occur due to their incompatibility.

If a limited area of plaster and laths has become detached from the joists, or if a moulded rib or other ornamental feature is loose, it is often possible to effect a local repair by screwing the plaster and lath into the joist from below, or into a short new piece of timber fixed across between the joists. Washers may be used to spread the area of support below the lath. The screw head should be set under the surface of the plaster with a wire gauze washer inserted to provide a key for plaster stopping. Non-ferrous fixings should be used.

Loose ribs may also be supported from above by copper-wire loops hung from metal rods above the ceiling or over any conveniently located timber supports.

Where local loss of key has occurred between laths or local areas of lath are defective, repairs may be achieved by cutting out the section of lath and forming a plaster "bridge" running between joists, with copper screws fixed into the joists to provide support.

Where large areas of laths have failed it is essential that proper support for the ceiling is provided from below before any action is taken. The decayed laths should then be cut off against the joists, taking relatively small areas at a time, and after cleaning and preparing the back of the plaster to reduce suction, a bed of retarded plaster of Paris should be laid out and worked into the old plaster. Support is then provided by pressing troughs of copper-wire mesh into the new plaster and securing them to the joists at each side. A second coat of plaster should then immediately be applied before the initial coat has set.

Repairs using low viscosity resin and glass fibre cloth in lieu of the above method should be approached with caution as this will effect a permanent bonding of the plaster and its timber supports, thus limiting future scope for action should further repairs be needed. This method does however, have the advantage of a considerable reduction of weight compared with the more traditional plaster of Paris method described above.

If ornamental features have been lost, new parts may be cast from moulds taken from adjacent original material and fixed up from below or hung from above by means of straps and rods fixed to the joists. If original material is not available from which to take a cast, photographic evidence may exist on which newly modelled ornament may be based after the preparation of detailed drawings. If moulds are formed from old moulded work by means of latex squeezes, the old work must first be thoroughly cleaned of old limewash, paint etc., any minor defects repaired beforehand, and the new moulded elements sharpened up before fixing. Otherwise there will be loss of sharpness, "life", and quality.

If cornices and other linear work were formed by running the basic outline in situ, and then applying cast or hand-moulded enrichments, it is particularly important to follow the same technique in repair or reinstatement. As much old work should be salvaged and refixed as possible; it is often feasible, for example, to detach old cast or moulded enrichments from a disintegrating cornice and refix them, making up the numbers as necessary on a newly run profile.

5

ENERGY CONSERVATION
AND DISASTER PLANNING

5.1 HEATING AND VENTILATION

It has long been well understood that the fabric of an historic building is maintained better by a modicum of heating. In previous centuries all rooms had a fireplace which allowed warmth to percolate through the structure via the flues, even if the occupants were not as warm as they might wish to be today. In addition, flues allowed the building to be naturally ventilated and the recent custom of blocking off fireplaces can only be deprecated. Flues must always be ventilated at top and bottom to avoid condensation and dampness occurring in the chimney which can damage decorative finishes as well as adding to the risk of rot in nearby woodwork.

Ideally all parts of a building should be heated to a low degree - not just the areas in occupation - and simple steps taken to insulate roofs (including lofts) to prevent warmth escaping through sarking and slates. But good ventilation of roof voids is particularly important to prevent outbreaks of fungal attack which is encouraged by modern demands for increased thermal comfort, so a balance has to be struck.

Routing of modern service through historic structures can take advantage of voids such as this above a coomb ceiling. (photo: I. Maxwell)

Sufficient ventilation can often be provided by simple and unobtrusive means, eg. by forming a slot at the eaves, incorporating a proprietary unit in the ridge, or replacing one of the slates with a wedge-shaped lead piece with an open mesh screen. Such provision is particularly important for churches, which are subject to intermittent heating and therefore condensation. Buildings where vernacular detailing of the roof is important are an exception here. (See 4.2.2 for special requirements of lead flat roofs.)

Likewise draughts from ill-fitting doors and windows can be reduced if not totally eradicated by draught-stripping and adjusting loose sashes and gaps under doors. Here, too, a degree of permanent ventilation is nevertheless desirable particularly in rooms where cooking and washing takes place and can often be achieved unobtrusively, for example by forming slots between the meeting rails or in the sash boxes of sash and case windows, or incorporating bronze mesh in the glazing pattern of a window. The provision of double-glazing is seldom without compromise to the historic fabric and its appearance, and secondary glazing may prove less intrusive. However, original fenestration should always be retained unaltered where possible.

The type of heating installation in an historic building will be normally influenced by economic and occupancy factors. Water-borne central heating systems are generally favoured for domestic and larger buildings such as churches, but the provision and siting of radiators must be done with sensitivity so as to minimise visual intrusion and damage to finishes. Temperatures should be controlled to ensure that drying out does not lead to excessive shrinkage of woodwork followed by the opening up of joints and alarming cracking in old panelling. Fan-assisted convectors can be useful where heating is intermittent or temperatures fluctuate. Portable heaters using liquid petroleum gas (LPG) should never be used as these produce a high volume of water vapour creating excessive condensation which can damage historic finishes.

Energy savings and an acceptable level of comfort can go hand-in-hand with the care and upkeep of a historic structure if it is ventilated, insulated where feasible, needless draughts are eliminated, and it is fitted with an unobtrusive heating system which provides general background warmth throughout with a possibility of boosting in specific areas when required.

5.2   FIRE PREVENTION

All the repair and restoration advice contained within this book can come to nothing if the building is not adequately protected against fire, and does not have a contingency plan for fire-fighting and salvage in the event of such a disaster overtaking it.

All historic buildings of any consequence should have both a fire protection assessment carried out and a Fire Action Plan drawn up - the latter being basically a "get-you-in" strategy for the fire brigade. This will ensure that the most valuable parts of the building are tackled first and any damage caused in fighting the fire is minimised.

The fire protection assessment should assess the risks that face the building and the range of passive fire precautions provided by the fabric which can be introduced to

Fire struck this historic building only a week after the completion of a comprehensive repair and restoration scheme.

minimise them. The risks may include such things as the likelihood of arson/vandalism, faulty electrical installations, lightning, defective chimneys and flues and last but most importantly, the presence of contractors on site which is when an historic building is often at its most vulnerable.

Consultation between the architect, surveyor, planning authority, insurance company and possibly the local fire authority will be necessary to arrive at appropriate fire precautions that do not compromise the historic structure or the character of historic rooms - particularly when there is any element of public risk. Each case will need to be the subject of specialist and individual assessment depending on the type of building. It is however, worthwhile pointing out that not all regulations can be directly applied to historic buildings without some unacceptable alteration if not damage to the fabric and finishes. Most authorities should be prepared to consider alternative solutions, eg., the non-enclosure of an historic staircase if an additional means of escape can be provided elsewhere, or the need to upgrade panelled doors to meet modern fire resistance standards if a smoke extract system can be installed to prevent smoke penetrating corridors and exit routes in the first place. Compromise may well prove possible where historic buildings are concerned, always accepting that the saving of human life must be the main priority.

The installation of sprinklers and other services into historic buildings has to be undertaken with the utmost care if damage is to be avoided.
(photo: I. Maxwell)

A Fire Action Plan (FAP) should be prepared for any historic building above standard domestic size and any building that contains valuable artefacts whether loose or attached to the structure. It is essential that it is prepared in conjunction with the Fire Brigade who will have to fight the fire in the building concerned, and is of no use whatsoever unless they have adopted it and are prepared to consult it in the event. It will show the most suitable route into the site for the fire tender and the location of any hydrants etc. It will indicate valuable doors and windows which should not be broken if any alternative means of access or entry can be found. It should prioritise rooms for attention (sleep risk being the first priority) and show which artefacts can be removed and which can be safeguarded in situ with protective haps etc. The latter is particularly important for painted ceilings, plasterwork etc., and fireplaces. The FAP should show a place of salvage to which contents can be easily removed without fouling fire-fighting lines. Ideally all information should be put on a good size plan of the building that can be read by torchlight and also in inclement weather.

The risk to an historic building when construction work is being carried out to it cannot be emphasised enough. A temporary fire assessment and FAP should be prepared specifically for the construction works in hand taking such items into account as: use of blowlamps, storage of flammable gas and other materials, temporary electrical wiring, operatives' smoking and use of stoves etc. A stringent hot-work permit regime should be operated by the contractor with a member of staff assigned to this specific task. Competent monitoring of risky building operations using flame or hot air equipment must be undertaken - ideally cold as opposed to hot methods should be adopted whenever possible - and monitoring should continue for a period of not less than two hours after the cessation of use. Additional fire-fighting equipment may need to be brought on site and all staff instructed in its operation.

5.3   SALVAGE

Should a fire disaster befall an historic building, or indeed another catastrophe such as a flood, hurricane or landslip, the disruption caused and the time during which the building is out of use can be minimised by proper contingency planning. Firstly it is important to take stock of the situation as coolly and calmly as possible and not rush into remedial works other than those which would prevent the disaster getting any worse, such as shoring or stabilising unsound or unsafe elements.

A pre-arranged photographic record of the building and its contents, the merit of which has been discussed earlier, will prove invaluable in such an event and should be kept either off-site or in a fire-proof cabinet. It may involve photogrammetry - which system produces line drawings of elevations etc., at a much lower cost than physical survey - or rectified photography which likewise allows scale sizes to be taken from prints and is particularly useful for contents. If the building is large enough aerial photography may also be justified.

Although it is difficult to assess the quantity, adequate salvage equipment should be kept on the premises and should include ladders, waterproof haps or sheeting, hard hats and most importantly gloves, as well as buckets and plastic bags. If the quality of the historic building demands the attention of archaeologists then an area must be set aside for them to gather undercover all fragments of plaster and timber etc., from specific areas or rooms. However unimportant the fragment may appear on the surface, it should be carefully bagged with its location noted.

Specialist advice should be sought on damaged artefact conservation particularly for fabrics and books. The latter can usually be freeze-dried in commercial freezers to forestall further deterioration and start the conservation process which if done expertly can restore books to a surprisingly acceptable if not pristine condition.

The building should be carefully and slowly dried to prevent needless warping or shrinkage. The use of dehumidifiers can sometimes be helpful as long as the area in which they are working can be fully sealed. It should also be kept in a state of security - not only against further collapse etc., but alert to the risk of vandals or looters. In winter the likelihood of frost damage to walls retaining moisture, which can cause stone to split on expansion, should not be overlooked.

BIBLIOGRAPHY

GENERAL

Ashurst, N, 1994 Cleaning of Historic Buildings (2 vols.), Donhead Publishing

Bowyer, J (ed), 1981 Handbook of Building Crafts in Conservation, Leeds, Hutchison

Caroe, A D R, 1949 Old Churches and Modern Craftsmanship, Oxford, Oxford University Press

Clifton-Taylor, A 1987 The Pattern of English Building, London, Faber & Faber

Davey, N, 1961 A History of Building Materials, Phoenix House

Dunbar, J G, 1966 The Historic Architecture of Scotland, London, Batsford

Edinburgh New Town Conservation Committee, 1979 The Care and Conservation of Georgian Houses, Edinburgh, Butterworth (new edition due, summer 1995)

English Nature, 1991 Bats in Roofs, A Guide for Surveyors, NCC

Everett, A, 1970 Mitchells Building Construction - Materials, London, Batsford

Fawcett, R, 1994 The Architectural History of Scotland: Scottish Architecture from the Accession of the Stewarts to the Reformation, EUP

Feilden, B M, 1982 Conservation of Historic Buildings, London. Butterworth, revised 1994.

Fenton, A, Walker, B, 1981 The Rural Architecture of Scotland John Donald

Fidler, J, 1980 Non-destructive Surveying Techniques for the Analysis of Historic Buildings, ASCHB Transaction, 5, 1980, 3-10

Gilbert J, Flint A, The Tenement Handbook, RIAS

Gomme, A, Walker, D, 1968 Architecture of Glasgow, London, Lund Humphries

Gow, I, 1992 The Scottish Interior, EUP

Highfield, D, Rehabilitation and Re-use of Old Buildings, Spon

Historic Scotland, 1993 Memorandum of Guidance on Listed Buildings and Conservation Areas, Historic Scotland

Historic Scotland, 1988, 2nd impression 1993 Scotland's Listed Buildings, A Guide to their Protection, Historic Scotland

Hollis, M, 1986 Surveying Buildings (2nd edn), Surveyors Publications, London

Insall, D W, 1973 The Care of Old Buildings Today, London, Architectural Press

International Council on Monuments and Sites, UK Committee, 1990 Guide to Recording, London, Butterworth

Kinniburgh, W, 1966 Dictionary of Building Materials, C R Books

Mc Gibbon, D, & Ross, T, 1887-1892 republished 1970, 1990 Castellated and Domestic Architecture (5 volumes), David Douglas, Mercat Press

McKean et al, 1990 Illustrated Architectural Guides, RIAS

Michell, Eleanor, 1988 Emergency repairs for historic buildings, London, English Heritage

Pierce, R, Coey, A and Oram, R, 1981 Taken for Granted The Royal Society of Ulster Architects and Historic Buildings Council

Pride, G L, 1975 Glossary of Scottish Building, Scottish Civic Trust

Powys, A R 1981 Repair of Ancient Buildings, London, Society for the Protection of Ancient Buildings

Richardson, B.A, 1991 Defects and Deteriorations in Buildings, Spon

Riches, A, Stell, G, 1992 Materials and Traditions in Scottish Building, SVBWG, Nic Allen

Rodwell, W, 1989 Church Archaeology, London, Batsford / English Heritage

Scottish Natural Heritage, Scotland's Wildlife: Bats, SNH

Scottish Vernacular Buildings Working Group, 1976 Building Construction in Scotland - some Historical and Regional Aspects, SVBWG

    Vernacular Building Materials, SVBWG

    Highland Vernacular Building, SVBWG

Smith, J F 1978 A Critical Biblography of Building Conservation, London, Mansell

Smith, L, 1985 Investigating Old Buildings, London, Batsford

Youngson, The Making of Classical Edinburgh,

STRUCTURES

Building Research Establishment, 1991 Digest 361, Why do buildings crack ? Watford, BRE

Highfield, D, 1991 The Construction of New Buildings behind Historic Facades, Spon

Macgregor, J E M, 1971 Outward Leaning Walls, SPAB Technical Pamphlet, 1, London, Society for the Protection of Ancient Buildings

ROOF COVERING

Ashurst, J, and N, 1988 Practical Building Conservation: Metals, English Heritage Technical Handbook, 4, Aldershot, Gower Technical Press

British Standards Institution, 1980 BS 2870, Specification for rolled copper and copper alloys, sheet, strip and foil

    1971 BS 680, Part 2, Roofing Slates (Metric Units)

    1990 BS 5534, Part 1, Code of Practice for Slating and Tiling (Design)

    1982 BS 1178, Specification for milled lead sheet for building purposes

    1985 BS 6561, Specification for zinc alloy sheet and strip for building

1970 (1988) CP 143, Part 12, Sheet Roof and Wall Coverings: Copper (Metric Units)

CP 143, Part 5, Zinc

Brocket, P, and Wright, A, 1986 The Care and Repair of Thatched Roofs, SPAB Technical Pamphlet, 10, London, Society for the Protection of Ancient Buildings

Copper Development Association, 1985 Copper in Roofing - Design and Installation, Potters Bar, CDA

Darby, K 1988 Church Roofing, London, Council for the Care of Churches

Lead Sheet Association, Lead Sheet Manual, Volume 1: Lead Sheet Flashings

Volume 2: Roofing and Cladding

Volume 3: Lead Sheet Details, London LDA

Walker, B, McGregor, C, Stark, G, 1994 Thatched Buildings: The Scottish Experience, in Traditional Architecture in Ireland, ed. B. Fhloinn and G Dennison, University College Dublin

West, R C, 1987 Thatch, a Manual for Owners, Surveyors, Architects and Builders, Newton Abbot, David & Charles

Zinc Development Association, 1971 Zinc in Building Design, London, ZDA

DAMP

Building Research Establishment, 1981 Digest 245, Rising Damp in Walls: Diagnosis and Treatment, Watford BRE

Thomas, A R, 1986 Treatment of Damp in Old Buildings SPAB Technical Pamphlet, 8, London, Society for the Protection of Ancient Buildings

TIMBER

Ashurst, J, and N, 1988 Practical Building Conservation: Wood, Glass and Resins, English Heritage Technical Handbook, 5, Aldershot, Gower Technical Press

Bravery, A F, Berry, R W, and Carey, J K, 1987 2nd Edition 1992 Recognising wood rot and insect damage in buildings, Watford, Building Research Establishment

British Standards Institution, 1975 BS 1282, Guide to the Choice, Use and Application of Wood Preservatives

British Wood-Preserving Association Technical Leaflets T 1: Fungal Decay in Buildings - Dry Rot and Wet Rot, London

T 2: Preservative Treatment of Timber, London

T3: Methods of Applying Preservatives, London

T4: The Preservation of Window Joinery, London

T5: Preservative Treatment Against Wood Borers, London

Brunskill, R W, 1985 Timber Building in Britain, Victor Gollanz Ltd

Building Research Establishment, Digest 296, Timbers: Their Natural Durability and Resistance to Preservative Treatment, Watford, BRE

Digest 299, Dry Rot: Its Recognition and Control, Watford, BRE

Historic Scotland, 1994 Performance Standards for Sash and Case Windows, Technical Advice Note 3, Crambeth Allen

Hughes, P, 1988 Patching Old Floor Boards, SPAB Information Sheet, 10, London, Society for the Protection of Ancient Buildings

Macgregor, J E M, 1973 Strengthening Timber Floors, SPAB Technical Pamphlet, 2, London, Society for the Protection of Ancient Buildings

Ridout, B V, 1992 Timber Decay in Buildings and its Treatment, Halesowen, West Midlands, Scientific and Educational Services Ltd.

Townsend, A, Clarke, M, 1991 The Repair of Wood Windows, SPAB Technical Pamphlet 13, HMSO

STONEWORK

Andrew, C, 1994 Stone Cleaning: a Guide for Practitioners, Historic Scotland and Robert Gordon University

Ashurst, J, 1977 Cleaning Stone and Brick, SPAB Technical Pamphlet, 4, London, Society for the Protection of Ancient Buildings

Ashurst, J, and N, 1988 Practical Building Conservation: Stone, English Heritage Technical Handbook, 1, Aldershot, Gower Technical Press

Ashurst, J, and Dimes, F G, 1977 Stone in Building - its Use and Potential Today, London, Architectural Press (reprinted 1984 by the Stone Federation)

Ashurst, J, Dimes, F G, and Honeyborne, D B, 1988 The Conservation of Building and Decorative Stone, London, Butterworth Scientific

Ashurst, N, 1994 Cleaning historic buildings, 2 volumes, Donhead

Bowley, M, J, 1975 Desalination of Stone: a Case Study, BRE Current Paper Series, CP 46/75, Watford, British Standards Institution, 1976 (1984) BS 5390, Code of Practice for Stone Masonry

1982 BS 6270, Part 1, Code of Practice for Cleaning and Surface Repairs of Buildings: Natural Stone, Cast Stone and Clay Calcium Silicate Brick Masonry (under revision, 1994)

Building Research Establishment, 1975 Digest 177, Decay and Conservation of Stone Masonry, Watford

1992 Digest 370, Control of Lichens, Moulds and Similar Growths, Watford, BRE

1983 Digest 269, The Selection of Natural Building Stone, Watford, BRE

1985 Digest 280, Cleaning External Surfaces of Buildings, Watford, BRE

Caroe, A D R, and Caroe, M B, 1984 Stonework: Maintenance and Surface Repair, London, Council for the Care of Churches

Cooke, R, Gibbs, G, 1993 Crumbling Heritage ? Studies of stone weathering in polluted atmospheres, Wetherby, National Power PLC and PowerGen PLC

Hughes, P, 1986 The Need for Old Buildings to 'Breathe', SPAB Information Sheet 4, London, Society for the Protection of Ancient Buildings

Leary, E, 1983 The Building Limestones of the British Isles, London, HMSO

    1986 The Building Sandstones of the British Isles, London, HMSO

Masonry Conservation Research Group, Robert Gordon Institute of Technology, 1991 Stonecleaning in Scotland: Literature Review, Research Reports 1-3, Research Summary, Aberdeen, Historic Scotland, Scottish Enterprise

Price, C A, 1975 The Decay and Preservation of Natural Building Stone, BRE Current Paper, CP 1/75, Watford, Building Research Establishment

    1981 Brethane Stone Preservative, BRE Curent Paper, CP 1.81, Watford, Building Research Establishment

    1984 The Consolidation of Limestone using a Lime Poultice and Limewater, Adhesive and Consolidants, London, International Institute for Conservation, 160-2 Stone Federation, 1986 Stone Federation Handbook and Directory, London

Rockwell, P, 1993 The Art of Stoneworking, A reference guide, CUP

Webster, R G M, (ed.) 1992 Stone cleaning and the nature, soiling and decay mechanisms of Stone, Proceedings of the International Conference held in Edinburgh, UK, 14-16 April 1992, Historic Scotland / Robert Gordon Institute of Technology, London, Donhead

BRICKWORK

Ashurst, J, and N, 1988 Practical Building Conservation: Brick, Terracotta and Earth, English Heritage Technical Handbook, 2, Aldershot, Gower Technical Press

Bidwell, T G, 1977 The Conservation of Brick Buildings - The Repair, Alteration and Restoration of Old Brickwork, London, Brick Development Association

Brunskill, R, 1990 Brick Building in Britain, Victor Gollanz

Building Research Establishment, 1991 Digest 359, Repairing Brick and Block Masonry, Watford, BRE

Williams G B A 1976 Chimneys in Old Buildings, SPAB Technical Pamphlet, 3, London, Society for the Protection of Ancient Buildings

    1983 Pointing Stone and Brick Walling, SPAB Technical Pamphlet, 5, London, Society for the Protection of Ancient Buildings

TERRACOTTA AND FAIENCE

Ashurst J, and N, 1988 Practical Building Conservation: Brick, Terracotta and Earth, English Heritage Technical Handbook, 2, Aldershot, Gower Technical Press

British Standards Institution, 1982 BS 6270, Part 1, Code of Practice for Cleaning and Surface Repair of Terracotta and Faience

Fidler, J, 1981 The Conservation of Architectural Terracotta and Faience, ASCHB Transactions, 6, 3-16

Prudhon, T H M, 1978 Architectural Terra Cotta: Analyzing the Deterioration Problems and Restoration Approaches, Technology and Conservation, 3, no 3, 30-8

RENDER AND HARLING

Ashurst, J, summer 1978 Mortars for Historic Buildings, Building Conservation

> 1983 Mortar, Plasters and Renders in Conservation, London, Ecclesiastical Architects and Surveyors' Association

Ashurst, J, and N, 1988 Practical Building Conservation: Plasters, Mortars and Renders, English Heritage Technical Handbook, 3, Aldershot, Gower Technical Press

Building Research Establishment, 1981 Digest 196, External Rendered Finishes, Watford, BRE

Cliver, E B, 1977 Tests for the Analysis of Mortar Samples, APT Bulletin, VI, no 1, 68-73

Historic Scotland, (1988 under revision) Preparation and Use of Lime Mortars, Historic Scotland Technical Advice Note 1, Historic Scotland

Schofield, J, 1986 Basic Limewash, SPAB Information Sheet, 1, London, Society for the Protection of Ancient Buildings

Townsend, A, 1989 Roughcast for Historic Buildings, SPAB Information Sheet, 11, London, Society for the Protection of Ancient Buildings

Wingate, M, 1994 An Introduction to Building Limes, SPAB Information Sheet, 9, London, Society for the Protection of Ancient Buildings

EARTH WALLS

Ashurst, J, and N, 1988 Practical Building Conservation: Brick, Terracotta and Earth, English Heritage Technical Handbook, 2, Aldershot, Gower Technical Press

Harrison, J R, 1984 The Mud Wall in England at the Close of the Vernacular Era, Transactions of the Ancient Monuments Society, 28

Hughes, R, March 1983 Material and Structural Behaviour of Soil Constructed Walls, Monumentum, 175-88

McCann, J, 1983 Clay and Cob Buildings, Shire Album 105, Aylesbury, Shire Publications

Pearson, G, 1992 Conservation of Clay and Chalk Buildings, London, Donhead

Walker, B, McGregor, C, Stark, G, 1994 Earth Buildings in Scotland and Ireland, in Out of Earth, ed. L Watson & S Harding, University of Plymouth

REINFORCED CONCRETE

Dinardo, C, Ballinghall, J R, 1988 Major Concrete Repairs and Restoration of Factory Structure: Uniroyal Ltd, Dumfries, Scotland, The Structural Engineer, 66, no 10.

IRONWORK

British Standards Institution, 1972 CP 3012, Cleaning and Preparation of Metal Surfaces

      1977 BS 5493, Code of Practice for Protective Coating of Iron and Steel Structures Against Corrosion

Evans, V R, 1972 The Rusting of Iron: Cause and Control, London, Edward Arnold

Hawkes, P W, 1971 Paints for Architectural Cast Iron, APT Journal X1, 17-35

Hoever, O, 1975 A Handbook of Wrought Iron from the Middle Ages to the End of the Eighteenth Century, London, Thames and Hudson

Lister, R, 1960 Decorative Cast Ironwork in Great Britain, London, G Bell and Sons

HISTORICAL GLASS

Burgoyne, I, and Scobie, R, 1983 Two Thousand Years of Flat Glass Making, Pilkington Bros plc

Dodsworth, R, 1982 Glass and Glass Making, Shire Album 83, Aylesbury, Shire Publications

Harrison Caviness, M, Stained Glass Before 1540 - An Annotated Biblography, Boston, Massachesetts, G K Hall & Co

Kerr, J, 1988 The Repair and Maintenance of Historic Glass, in Practical Building Conservation: Wood, Glass and Resins (J and N Ashurst), English Heritage Technical Handbook, 5, Aldershot, Gower Technical Press, ch 2

Kerr, J 1991 The Repair and Maintenance of Glass in Churches, Church House

Lee, L, Seddon, G, and Stephens F, 1976 Stained Glass, London, Mitchell Beazley

Newton, R G, 1982 The Deterioration and Conservation of Painted Glass: A Critical Biblography, published for the British Academy by Oxford University Press as Corpus Vitrearum, Medii Aevi Great Britain, Occasional Paper II

Van den Bemden, Y, and De Henau, P, 1987 Les Vitraux Anciens - Note Technique Visant A L'Establissement D'un Cahier Des Charges Type Pour La Restauration Des Vitraux Anciens Et De Valeur, L'Institut Royal de Patrimoine Artistique et du Corpus Vitrearum de Belgique

PLASTERWORK

Ashurst J, 1983 Mortars, Plasters and Renders in Conservation, London, Ecclesiastical Architects' and Surveyors' Association

Ashurst J, and N, 1988 Practical Building Conservation: Plasters, Mortars and Renders, English Heritage Technical Handbook, 3, Aldershot, Gower Technical Press

Beard, G, 1983 Stucco and Decorative Plasterwork in Europe, London, Thames and Hudson

Drury, P J, 1984 Joseph Rose Senior's Workshops at Audley End: Aspects of the Development of Decorative Plasterwork Technology in Britain during the Eighteenth Century, Antiquaries Journal, LXIV, 62-83

Historic Scotland, Simpson and Brown ed., 1994 Conservation of Plasterwork, A guide to the principles of conserving and repairing historic plasterwork, Historic Scotland Technical Advice Note 2, Crambeth Allen

Pegg and Stagg, 1976 Plastering - A Craftsman's Encylopaedia, London, Crosby Lockwood Staples

Stagg, W D, and Mastons, R, 1983 Decorative Plasterwork - Its Repair and Restoration, London, Orion Books

PAINT

Bristow, I, 1981a The Redecoration of the Dulwich Picture Gallery 1980-81, ASCHB Transactions, 6, 33-6

1981b Repainting Eighteenth-Century Interiors, ASCHB Transactions, 6, 25-33

1984 The Casino at Marino, Part II: An Account of the Technical Investigation of the Paintwork and Redecoration of the Interior, ASCHB Transactions, 9, 29-44

1986a Redecorating Your Church, London, Council for the Care of Churches

1986b The Restoration of Sir John Soane's Colour Scheme in the Breakfast Room at Pitzhanger Manor, Ealing, ASCHB Transactions, 11, 43-8

1973 25 Painting Woodwork, HMSO

Building Research Establishment, 1990 Digest 354, Painting Exterior Wood, Watford, BRE

Scholfield, J, 1986 Basic Limewash, SPAB Information Sheet, 1, London, Society for the Protection of Ancient Buildings

Thornton, P, 1984 Authentic Decor, London, Weidenfield and Nicolson

ENERGY CONSERVATION

RICS, Energy Appraisal of Existing Buildings: A Handbook for Surveyors

FIRE PROTECTION etc.

Allen, N L, 1988 Protection of Churches against lightning, London, Council for the Care of Curches

Bailey, Sir A D, et al, 1993 Fire Protection Measures for Royal Palaces, DNH, HMSO

Fishlock, M 1992 The Great Fire at Hampton Court, Herbert Press

Kidd, S, ed. Heritage Under Fire, A guide to the protection of historic buildings, London: UK Working Party on Fire Safety in Historic Buildings, Fire Protection Association, (new ed. 1995)

The Fire Protection Association, 1992 Fire Protection in Old Buildings and Historic Town Centres, London, FPA

ACKNOWLEDGEMENTS

The English Heritage first edition included a list of acknowledgements which, since much of the text and intention remain the same, is reproduced again here: Andrew Anderson, Mrs Corinne Bennett, Peter Bird, Stephen Bond of the Royal Institute of Chartered Surveyors, John Bowles of the Redundant Churches Fund, Dr Ian Bristow, Mrs Patricia Brock, Peter Brownhill, High Cantlie, Martin Caroe, Ian Curry, Christopher Dalton of the Redundant Churches Fund, Keith Darby, John Deal, Edward Diestelkamp of the National Trust, Anthony Drew-Edwards, Professor James Dunbar-Naismith, John Earl, Richard Eckersley of the Department of the Environment Conservation Unit, Terry Empson of the Historic Houses Association, Harry Fairhurst, Alan Ford, Daryl Fowler, John Goom, Stanley Harrison of the National Trust, Anthony Hartridge, C J Howells of British Waterways, Philip Hughes, Geoffrey Hutton, Ronald Jones, Colin Kerr, Michael King, Dr Derek Linstrum, John Maggs, Peter Marshall. Ingval Maxwell of Historic Buildings and Monuments, Scotland, Rodney Melville, Clive Mercer, Anthony New, Richard Oram of Historic Monuments and Buildings Branch, Department of the Environment for Northern Ireland, Thomas Overbury, Paul Pearn, Norman Phillips, Mrs Jane Priestman of British Rail, Robert Read, Michael Reardon, Trevor Roberts, Henry Rushton, Matthew Saunders of the Ancient Monuments Society, James Scott, James Simpson, Ian Stainburn, Robert Tolley, Andrew Townsend, Phillip Venning of the Society for the Protection of Ancient Buildings, David Walker of Historic Buildings and Monuments, Scotland, John Wheatley, Kenneth Wiltshire, and R A Wright of the British Wood Preserving and Damp-proofing Association. The layout of the first edition was by Andrew McLaren. The second edition, edited by Dr Philip Whitbourn, acknowledges David Brock, Rebecca Child, John Fidler, John Figg of Ove Arup and Partners, Ray Harrison, David Heath, Ian Hume, Francis Kelly, John McAslan, Nicolas Molyneux, Ron Phillips, Arnold Root, Andrew Townsend and Michael Wingate.

In addition, Historic Scotland would like to thank the following for their helpful comments and advice: Vanessa Brand (EH), Jacky Chalmers (EDAS), David Heath (EH), David Henrie (HS photographers unit), Lothian and Borders Fire Brigade (Div Officer Simpson), Charles McKean (RIAS), A McKee (Glass of Paisley), Patrick Ross-Smith, Andrew Wright (RIAS).

NOTES

NOTES

NOTES